MW00837825

MINIMAX METHODS
IN CRITICAL POINT THEORY
WITH APPLICATIONS
TO DIFFERENTIAL EQUATIONS

Conference Board of the Mathematical Sciences
REGIONAL CONFERENCE SERIES IN MATHEMATICS

supported by the
National Science Foundation

Number 65

MINIMAX METHODS IN CRITICAL POINT THEORY WITH APPLICATIONS TO DIFFERENTIAL EQUATIONS

Paul H. Rabinowitz

Published for the
Conference Board of the Mathematical Sciences
by the
American Mathematical Society
Providence, Rhode Island

Expository Lectures
from the CBMS Regional Conference
held at the University of Miami
January 9–13, 1984

Research supported in part by National Science Foundation Grant DMS-8303355.

1980 *Mathematics Subject Classifications* (1985 *Revision*). Primary 34C25, 35J60, 47H15, 58E05, 58E07, 58F05, 70H05, 70H30.

Library of Congress Cataloging-in-Publication Data

Rabinowitz, Paul H.

Minimax methods in critical point theory with applications to differential equations.

(Regional conference series in mathematics, ISSN 0160-7642; no. 65)

"Expository lectures from the CBMS Regional Conference held at the University of Miami, January 9–13, 1984"–T.p. verso.

"Supported by the National Science Foundation."

Bibliography: p.

1. Critical point theory (Mathematical analysis)–Congresses. 2. Maxima and minima–Congresses. 3. Differential equations, Elliptic–Congresses. I. Conference Board of the Mathematical Sciences. II. Title. III. Series.

QA1.R33 no. 65 510s [515.3′3] 86-7847
[QA614.7]
ISBN 0-8218-0715-3 (alk. paper)

Copying and reprinting. Individual readers of this publication, and nonprofit libraries acting for them, are permitted to make fair use of the material, such as to copy an article for use in teaching or research. Permission is granted to quote brief passages from this publication in reviews, provided the customary acknowledgment of the source is given.

Republication, systematic copying, or multiple reproduction of any material in this publication (including abstracts) is permitted only under license from the American Mathematical Society. Requests for such permission should be addressed to the Executive Director, American Mathematical Society, P.O. Box 6248, Providence, Rhode Island 02940.

The owner consents to copying beyond that permitted by Sections 107 or 108 of the U.S. Copyright Law, provided that a fee of $1.00 plus $.25 per page for each copy be paid directly to the Copyright Clearance Center, Inc., 21 Congress Street, Salem, Massachusetts 01970. When paying this fee please use the code 0160-7642/86 to refer to this publication. This consent does not extend to other kinds of copying, such as copying for general distribution, for advertising or promotion purposes, for creating new collective works, or for resale.

Copyright © 1986 by the American Mathematical Society. All rights reserved.
Reprinted with corrections 1988
Printed in the United States of America
The American Mathematical Society retains all rights
except those granted to the United States Government.
The paper used in this book is acid-free and falls within the guidelines
established to ensure permanence and durability. ♾

Contents

Preface

This monograph is an expanded version of a CBMS series of lectures delivered in Miami in January, 1984. As in the lectures, our goal is to provide an introduction to minimax methods in critical point theory and their application to problems in differential equations. The presentation of the abstract minimax theory is essentially self-contained. Most of the applications are to semilinear elliptic partial differential equations and a basic knowledge of linear elliptic theory is required for this material. An overview is given of the subject matter in Chapter 1 and a detailed study is carried out in the chapters that follow.

Many friends have contributed to my study and organization of this material. I thank in particular Antonio Ambrosetti, Abbas Bahri, Vieri Benci, Henri Berestycki, Haïm Brezis, Michael Crandall, Edward Fadell, Suffian Husseini, Jürgen Moser, and Louis Nirenberg for their inspiration, encouragement, and advice. The CBMS conference was hosted by the Mathematics Department of the University of Miami. Further thanks are due to the members of the department, especially to Shair Ahmad and Alan Lazer for their efficient handling of the meeting and their kind hospitality.

1. An Overview

A focus of these lectures is the existence of critical points of real valued functionals. The most familiar example occurs when we have a continuously differentiable map $g\colon \mathbf{R}^n \to \mathbf{R}$. A critical point of g is a point ξ at which $g'(\xi)$, the Fréchet derivative of g, vanishes. The simplest sort of critical points of g are its global or local maxima or minima.

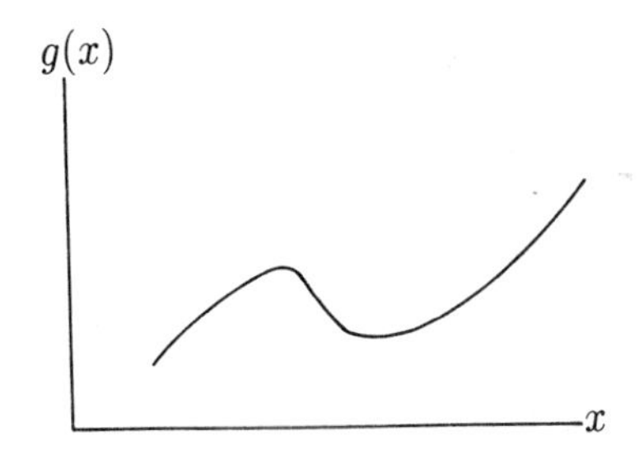

The setting in which we will study critical point theory is an infnite dimensional generalization of the above. Let E be a real Banach space. A mapping I of E to $\mathbf{R}$ will be called a functional. To make precise what we mean by a critical point of I, recall that I is Fréchet differentiable at $u \in E$ if there exists a continuous linear map $L = L(u)\colon E \to \mathbf{R}$ satisfying: for any $\varepsilon > 0$, there is a $\delta = \delta(\varepsilon, u) > 0$ such that $|I(u+v) - I(u) - Lv| \le \varepsilon\|v\|$ for all $\|v\| \le \delta$. The mapping L is usually denoted by $I'(u)$. Note that $I'(u) \in E^*$, the dual space of E. A *critical point* u of I is a point at which $I'(u) = 0$, i.e.

$$I'(u)\varphi = 0$$

for all $\varphi \in E$. The value of I at u is then called a *critical value* of I.

In applications to differential equations, critical points correspond to weak solutions of the equation. Indeed this fact makes critical point theory an important existence tool in studying differential equations. As an example consider the linear elliptic boundary value problem

$$\begin{aligned} -\Delta u &= f(x), \qquad x \in \Omega, \\ u &= 0, \qquad x \in \partial\Omega, \end{aligned} \tag{1.1}$$

where here and in future examples Ω denotes a bounded domain in $\mathbf{R}^n$ whose boundary, $\partial\Omega$, is a smooth manifold. Suppose $f \in C(\overline{\Omega})$. A function u is a classical solution of (1.1) if $u \in C^2(\Omega) \cap C(\overline{\Omega})$. For such a solution, multiplying (1.1) by $\varphi \in C_0^\infty(\Omega)$ yields

$$\int_\Omega (\nabla u \cdot \nabla\varphi - f\varphi)\, dx = 0 \tag{1.2}$$

after an integration by parts. Let $W_0^{1,2}(\Omega)$ denote the closure of $C_0^\infty(\Omega)$ with respect to

$$\|u\|_{W_0^{1,2}} \equiv \left(\int_\Omega |\nabla u|^2\, dx\right)^{1/2}$$

If $u \in W_0^{1,2}(\Omega)$ and satisfies (1.2) for all $\varphi \in C_0^\infty(\Omega)$, then u is said to be a weak solution of (1.1). By our above remarks, any classical solution of (1.1) is a weak solution. Under slightly stronger hypotheses on f (e.g. f Hölder continuous) the converse is also true. Choosing $E \equiv W_0^{1,2}(\Omega)$, set

$$I(u) \equiv \int_\Omega (\tfrac{1}{2}|\nabla u|^2 - fu)\, dx. \tag{1.3}$$

It is not difficult to verify that I is Fréchet differentiable on E and

$$I'(u)\varphi = \int_\Omega (\nabla u \cdot \nabla\varphi - f\varphi)\, dx \tag{1.4}$$

for $\varphi \in E$. Thus u is a critical point of I if and only if u is a weak solution of (1.1).

As was noted earlier, when $E = \mathbf{R}^n$ the most familiar sorts of critical points obtained are maxima or minima. In these lectures we will be dealing mainly with functionals which may not be bounded from above or below even modulo finite dimensional subspaces or submanifolds. Such "indefinite" functionals may not possess any local maxima or minima other than trivial ones. For example let $\Omega = (0,\pi) \subset \mathbf{R}$, $E = W_0^{1,2}([0,\pi])$, and

$$I(u) = \int_0^\pi (\tfrac{1}{2}|u'|^2 - \tfrac{1}{4}u^4)\, dx, \tag{1.5}$$

where $' \equiv d/dx$. It is not difficult to show that I is differentiable on E and has $u = 0$ as a local minimum. For any other $u \in E$ and $\alpha \in \mathbf{R}$,

$$I(\alpha u) = \int_0^\pi \left(\frac{\alpha^2}{2}|u'|^2 - \frac{\alpha^4}{4}u^4\right) dx \to -\infty$$

as $|\alpha| \to \infty$ so I is not bounded from below. Furthermore for each $k \in \mathbf{N}$, $\sin kx \in E$, and

$$I(\sin kx) \geq \frac{\pi}{4}k^2 - \frac{\pi}{4} \to \infty$$

as $k \to \infty$ so I is not bounded from above. Thus it is not obvious that I possesses any critical points other than the trivial one $u \equiv 0$. Nevertheless we will see later as an application of the Mountain Pass Theorem that I possesses positive critical values and the same thing is true for higher dimensional versions of (1.5).

As a second example of an indefinite functional, consider the Hamiltonian system of ordinary differential equations

$$\frac{dp}{dt} = -H_q(p,q), \qquad \frac{dq}{dt} = H_p(p,q), \tag{1.6}$$

where $H\colon \mathbf{R}^{2n} \to \mathbf{R}$ is smooth, and p and q are n-tuples. We are interested in periodic solutions of (1.6). Taking the period to be 2π and choosing E to be an appropriate space of 2π periodic functions, solutions of (1.6) are critical points of

$$I(p,q) = \int_0^{2\pi} [p(t)\cdot \dot{q}(t) - H(p(t),q(t))]\, dt. \tag{1.7}$$

(This will be made precise in Chapter 6.) To see the indefinite nature of (1.7), suppose $n = 1$. Taking $p_k(t) = \sin kt$ and $q_k(t) = -\cos kt$ shows $I(p_k, q_k) = k\pi +$ bounded term $\to \pm\infty$ as $k \to \pm\infty$. Thus I is not bounded from above or below. Despite this, as we shall see later, minimax methods can be applied to the functional (1.7) to obtain periodic solutions of (1.6).

There are at least two sets of methods that have been developed to find critical points of functionals: (i) Morse theory and its generalizations and (ii) minimax theory. For material on "classical" Morse theory, see e.g. [**Mi**, **S2**, **Ch2**]. Generalized Morse theories and the so-called Conley index can be found in the CBMS monograph of Conley [**CC**] (see also [**Sm**]). Our lectures will focus on minimax theory. This subject originated in work of Ljusternik and Schnirelman [**LLS**] although it certainly had antecedents (see e.g. [**Bi**]).

What are minimax methods? These are methods that characterize a critical value c of a functional I as a minimax over a suitable class of sets S:

$$c = \inf_{A\in S} \max_{u\in A} I(u). \tag{1.8}$$

There is no recipe for choosing S. In any given situation the choice must reflect some qualitative change in the topological nature of the level sets of I, i.e. the sets $I^{-1}(s)$ for s near c. Thus obtaining and characterizing a critical value c as in (1.8) is something of an ad hoc process.

The Mountain Pass Theorem is the first minimax result that we will study. Its statement involves a useful technical assumption—the Palais-Smale condition—that occurs repeatedly in critical point theory. Suppose E is a real Banach space. Let $C^1(E,\mathbf{R})$ denote the set of functionals that are Fréchet differentiable and whose Fréchet derivatives are continuous on E. For $I \in C^1(E,\mathbf{R})$, we say I satisfies the Palais-Smale condition (henceforth denoted by (PS)) if any sequence $(u_m) \subset E$ for which $I(u_m)$ is bounded and $I'(u_m) \to 0$ as $m \to \infty$ possesses a convergent subsequence. The (PS) condition is a convenient way to build some "compactness" into the functional I. Indeed observe that (PS) implies that $K_c \equiv \{u \in E | I(u) = c \text{ and } I'(u) = 0\}$, i.e. the set of critical points having critical value c, is compact for any $c \in \mathbf{R}$. We will see many examples later of when (PS) is satisfied.

Let B_r denote the open ball in E of radius r about 0 and let ∂B_r denote its boundary. Now the Mountain Pass Theorem can be stated.

THEOREM. *Let E be a real Banach space and $I \in C^1(E, \mathbf{R})$. Suppose I satisfies (PS), $I(0) = 0$,*

(I_1) there exist constants $\rho, \alpha > 0$ such that $I|_{\partial B_\rho} \geq \alpha$, and

(I_2) there is an $e \in E \setminus \partial B_\rho$ such that $I(e) \leq 0$.

Then I possesses a critical value $c \geq \alpha$ which can be characterized as

$$c = \inf_{g \in \Gamma} \max_{u \in g[0,1]} I(u),$$

where

$$\Gamma = \{g \in C([0,1], E) | g(0) = 0, g(1) = e\}.$$

This result is due to Ambrosetti and Rabinowitz [**AR**]. On a heuristic level, the theorem says if a pair of points in the graph of I are separated by a mountain range, there must be a mountain pass containing a critical point between them. Although the statement of the theorem does not require it, in applications it is generally the case that I has a local minimum at 0.

A second geometrical example of a minimax result is the following Saddle Point Theorem [**R4**]:

THEOREM. *Let E be a real Banach space such that $E = V \oplus X$, where V is finite dimensional. Suppose $I \in C^1(E, \mathbf{R})$, satisfies (PS), and*

(I_3) there exists a bounded neighborhood, D, of 0 in V and a constant α such that $I|_{\partial D} \leq \alpha$, and

(I_4) there is a constant $\beta > \alpha$ such that $I|_X \geq \beta$.

Then I has a critical value $c \geq \beta$. Moreover c can be characterized as

$$c = \inf_{S \in \Gamma} \max_{u \in S} I(u),$$

where

$$\Gamma = \{S = h(\overline{D}) | h \in C(\overline{D}, E) \text{ and } h = \mathrm{id} \text{ on } \partial D\}.$$

Here heuristically c is the minimax of I over all surfaces modelled on D and which share the same boundary. Unlike the Mountain Pass Theorem, in applications of the Saddle Point Theorem generally no critical points of I are known initially. Note that (I_3) and (I_4) are satisfied if I is convex on X, concave on V, and appropriately coercive. Indeed the Saddle Point Theorem was motivated by earlier results of that nature due to Ahmad, Lazer, and Paul [**ALP**] and Castro and Lazer [**CL**].

Both of the above theorems, generalizations, and applications will be treated in Chapters 2–6. In particular in a somewhat more restrictive setting both the Mountain Pass Theorem and Saddle Point Theorem can be interpreted as special cases of a more general critical point theorem which is proved in Chapter 5.

Much of the remainder of these lectures will be devoted to the study of variational problems in which symmetries play a role. To be more precise, suppose

E is a real Banach space, $\mathbf{G}$ is a group of transformations of E into E, and $I \in C^1(E, \mathbf{R})$. We say I is invariant under $\mathbf{G}$ if $I(gu) = I(u)$ for all $g \in \mathbf{G}$ and $u \in E$. As a first example, consider (1.5). It is invariant under $\mathbf{G} \equiv \{\mathrm{id}, -\mathrm{id}\}$, where id denotes the identity map on E. Note that we can identify $\mathbf{G}$ with $\mathbf{Z}_2$. More generally if $p(x, \xi)$ is continuous on $[0, \pi] \times \mathbf{R}$, is odd in ξ, and $P(x, \xi) = \int_0^\xi p(x, t)\, dt$, then

$$I(u) = \int_0^\pi [\tfrac{1}{2}|u'|^2 - P(x, u)]\, dx \tag{1.9}$$

is invariant under $\mathbf{G}$. As another example consider (1.7), recalling for this case that functions in E are 2π periodic. Let $\theta \in [0, 2\pi)$, $z = (p, q) \in E$, $(g_\theta z)(t) \equiv z(t + \theta)$, and $\mathbf{G} \equiv \{g_\theta | \theta \in [0, 2\pi)\}$. Then it is easy to see that Γ is invariant under $\mathbf{G}$. Moreover $\mathbf{G}$ can be identified with S^1.

The above examples show that functionals invariant under a group of symmetries arise in a natural fashion. It is often the case that such functionals possess multiple critical points. Indeed results of this type are among the most fascinating in minimax theory. The first example of such a theorem goes back to early work of Ljusternik and Schnirelman [**LLS**]. They studied a constrained variational problem, i.e. I restricted to a manifold (which must be invariant under $\mathbf{G}$) and proved

THEOREM. *If $I \in C^1(\mathbf{R}^n, \mathbf{R})$ and is even, then $I|_{S^{n-1}}$ possesses at least n distinct pairs of critical points.*

Subsequently other researchers extended this result to an infinite dimensional setting.

Another multiplicity result is provided by the following $\mathbf{Z}_2$ symmetric version of the Mountain Pass Theorem [**AR, R2**]:

THEOREM. *Let E be a real Banach space and $I \in C^1(E, \mathbf{R})$ with I even. Suppose $I(0) = 0$ and I satisfies (PS), (I_1), and*

(I_2') for all finite dimensional subspaces $\tilde{E} \subset E$, there is an $R = R(\tilde{E})$ such that $I(u) \le 0$ for $u \in \tilde{E} \setminus B_{R(\tilde{E})}$.

Then I possesses an unbounded sequence of critical values.

In order to exploit symmetries of I, one needs a tool to measure the size of symmetric sets, i.e. subsets of E invariant under $\mathbf{G}$. Such a tool is provided by the notion of an index theory. With the aid of such theories, minimax characterizations can be given for the critical points obtained in the two theorems just cited. Index theories will be discussed in Chapter 7 and applied to constrained and unconstrained variational problems in Chapters 8–9. In particular we will see that generalized versions of (1.5) satisfy the hypotheses of the symmetric Mountain Pass Theorem and possess an unbounded sequence of critical points.

The next question we will study is what happens to a functional which is invariant under a group of symmetries when a perturbation is made which destroys the symmetry. No general theory has been developed yet to treat such matters and we will confine our attention to an example from partial differential equations in Chapter 10.

Our final topic, covered in Chapter 11, concerns applications of minimax methods to bifurcation problems. Such problems are of interest since bifurcation phenomena occur in a wide variety of settings in nature. Consider the map $\mathbf{F}\colon \mathbf{R}\times E \to E$, where

$$\mathbf{F}(\lambda, u) = Lu + H(u) - \lambda u, \tag{1.10}$$

E is a real Banach space, $\lambda \in \mathbf{R}$, $u \in E$, L is a continuous linear map of E into E, and $H \in C^1(E, E)$ with $H(u) = o(\|u\|)$ as $u \to 0$. Note that $\mathbf{F}(\lambda, 0) = 0$ for all $\lambda \in \mathbf{R}$. We call these zeros of $\mathbf{F}$ *trivial solutions* of $\mathbf{F}(\lambda, u) = 0$. A point $(\mu, 0) \in \mathbf{R}\times E$ is called a *bifurcation point* for $\mathbf{F}$ if every neighborhood of $(\mu, 0)$ contains nontrivial solutions of $\mathbf{F}(\lambda, u) = 0$. It is well known—see Chapter 11—that a necessary condition for $(\mu, 0)$ to be a bifurcation point is that $\mu \in \sigma(L)$, the spectrum of L. Simple counterexamples show this necessary condition is not sufficient. However in Chapter 11, it will be shown that if (1.10) corresponds to an equation of the form $I'(u) = 0$, $\mu \in \sigma(L)$ is also a sufficient condition for $(\mu, 0)$ to be a bifurcation point. Other sharper results will give more information about the nontrivial solutions of $\mathbf{F}(\lambda, u) = 0$ for (λ, u) near $(\mu, 0)$ both as a function of $\|u\|$ and as a function of λ.

Lastly there are two appendices. The first, Appendix A, is mainly concerned with an important tool called the Deformation Theorem. It is used to help prove all of our abstract critical point theorems. Appendix B contains some technical results which are useful in verifying abstract conditions like $I \in C^1(E, \mathbf{R})$ or (PS) in a partial differential equations setting.

Some other sources of material on minimax methods and critical point theory in general are [**BW**, **Bg**, **Ch2**, **CC**, **K**, **LLS**, **Mi**, **N2**, **P2**, **R2**, **S2**, **Va**].

2. The Mountain Pass Theorem and Some Applications

In this chapter we will prove the usual version of the Mountain Pass Theorem and give some applications to semilinear elliptic partial differential equations. The ideas involved in the proof of the Mountain Pass Theorem are very simple. A key ingredient is the so-called Deformation Theorem. This latter result plays an important role in all of our abstract minimax results. Since it is rather lengthy and technical in nature, we have relegated it to Appendix A (see Theorem A.4). The following special case is sufficient for the proof of the Mountain Pass Theorem.

PROPOSITION 2.1. *Let E be a real Banach space. Suppose $I \in C^1(E, \mathbf{R})$, and satisfies (PS). For $s, c \in \mathbf{R}$, set $K_c \equiv \{u \in E | I(u) = c$ and $I'(u) = 0\}$ and $A_s = \{u \in E | I(u) \leq s\}$. If c is not a critical value of I, given any $\bar{\varepsilon} > 0$, there exists an $\varepsilon \in (0, \bar{\varepsilon})$ and $\eta \in C([0,1] \times E, E)$ such that:*
$1°$ $\eta(1, u) = u$ if $I(u) \notin [c - \bar{\varepsilon}, c + \bar{\varepsilon}]$,
$2°$ $\eta(1, A_{c+\varepsilon}) \subset A_{c-\varepsilon}$.

Now we can prove

THEOREM 2.2 (MOUNTAIN PASS THEOREM [**AR**]). *Let E be a real Banach space and $I \in C^1(E, \mathbf{R})$ satisfying (PS). Suppose $I(0) = 0$ and*
(I_1) there are constants $\rho, \alpha > 0$ such that $I|_{\partial B_\rho} \geq \alpha$, and
(I_2) there is an $e \in E \setminus \overline{B}_\rho$ such that $I(e) \leq 0$.
Then I possesses a critical value $c \geq \alpha$. Moreover c can be characterized as

$$c = \inf_{g \in \Gamma} \max_{u \in g([0,1])} I(u), \tag{2.3}$$

where

$$\Gamma = \{g \in C([0,1], E) | g(0) = 0, g(1) = e\}.$$

PROOF. The definition of c shows that $c < \infty$. If $g \in \Gamma$, $g([0,1]) \cap \partial B_\rho \neq \emptyset$. Therefore

$$\max_{u \in g([0,1])} I(u) \geq \inf_{w \in \partial B_\rho} I(w) \geq \alpha$$

via (I_1). Consequently $c \geq \alpha$. Suppose that c is not a critical value of I. Then Proposition 2.1 with $\bar{\varepsilon} = \alpha/2$ yields $\varepsilon \in (0, \bar{\varepsilon})$ and η as in that result. Choose

$g \in \Gamma$ such that

$$\max_{u \in g([0,1])} I(u) \leq c + \varepsilon \tag{2.4}$$

and consider $h(t) \equiv \eta(1, g(t))$. Clearly $h \in C([0,1], E)$. Also $g(0) = 0$ and $I(0) = 0 < \alpha/2 \leq c - \bar{\varepsilon}$ imply $h(0) = 0$ by 1° of Proposition 2.1. Similarly $g(1) = e$ and $I(e) \leq 0$ imply that $h(1) = e$. Consequently $h \in \Gamma$ and by (2.3),

$$c \leq \max_{u \in h([0,1])} I(u). \tag{2.5}$$

But by (2.4), $g([0,1]) \subset A_{c+\varepsilon}$ so 2° of Proposition 2.1 implies $h([0,1]) \subset A_{c-\varepsilon}$, i.e.

$$\max_{u \in h([0,1])} I(u) \leq c - \varepsilon, \tag{2.6}$$

contrary to (2.5). Thus c is a critical value of I.

Although the above proof is very simple, one sees the basic ingredients of a minimax theorem: (i) a family of sets which is chosen to exploit the properties of I and which is invariant under the deformation map $\eta(1, \cdot)$, (ii) a minimax value c obtained from this family of sets, (iii) topological arguments giving some estimates for c (and showing in particular that c is finite), (iv) an indirect argument based on the Deformation Theorem proving that c is a critical value of I. This framework will be used repeatedly in these lectures. As an almost trivial application of some of these ideas we have

THEOREM 2.7. *Let E be a real Banach space and $I \in C^1(E, \mathbf{R})$ satisfying (PS). If I is bounded from below, then*

$$c \equiv \inf_E I \tag{2.8}$$

is a critical value of I.

PROOF. Clearly c is finite. Set $S = \{\{x\} | x \in E\}$, i.e. S is a collection of sets each consisting of one point. Trivially we have

$$c = \inf_{K \in S} \max_{u \in K} I(u).$$

Now for any choice of $\bar{\varepsilon}$, e.g. $\bar{\varepsilon} = 1$, since $\eta(1, \cdot)$ as given by Proposition 2.1 maps S into S, the argument of Theorem 2.2 shows c is a critical value of I.

The remainder of this section consists of several applications of the Mountain Pass Theorem to boundary value problems for semilinear elliptic partial differential equations. Consider

$$\begin{aligned} -\Delta u &= p(x, u), \qquad x \in \Omega, \\ u &= 0, \qquad x \in \partial\Omega, \end{aligned} \tag{2.9}$$

where $\Omega \subset \mathbf{R}^n$ is a bounded domain whose boundary is a smooth manifold. In (2.9) and later applications, $-\Delta$ could be replaced by a more general second order divergence structure uniformly elliptic operator. However we prefer to minimize such technicalities.

The function p will always be assumed to satisfy

(p_1) $p(x, \xi) \in C(\overline{\Omega} \times \mathbf{R}, \mathbf{R})$, and

(p_2) there are constants $a_1, a_2 \geq 0$ such that

$$|p(x, \xi)| \leq a_1 + a_2|\xi|^s,$$

where $0 \leq s < (n+2)/(n-2)$ if $n > 2$.

If $n = 1$, (p_2) can be dropped while if $n = 2$, it suffices that

$$|p(x, \xi)| \leq a_1 \exp \varphi(\xi),$$

where $\varphi(\xi)\xi^{-2} \to 0$ as $|\xi| \to \infty$. The reason for such structural conditions is the following: The functional associated with (2.9) is

$$I(u) = \int_\Omega (\tfrac{1}{2}|\nabla u|^2 - P(x, u))\, dx, \tag{2.10}$$

where $P(x, \xi) = \int_0^\xi p(x, t)\, dt$. A natural space in which to treat (2.10) is $E = W_0^{1,2}(\Omega)$, the closure of $C_0^\infty(\Omega)$ with respect to

$$\left(\int_\Omega (|\nabla u|^2 + u^2)\, dx\right)^{1/2}$$

By the Poincaré inequality, there is a constant $\mu_1 > 0$ such that

$$\mu_1 \int_\Omega u^2\, dx \leq \int_\Omega |\nabla u|^2\, dx$$

for all $u \in E$. Hence we can and will take as norn in E,

$$\|u\| \equiv \left(\int_\Omega |\nabla u|^2\, dx\right)^{1/2} \tag{2.11}$$

In order to apply Theorem 2.2 to the functional I given by (2.10), we have to know that $I \in C^1(E, \mathbf{R})$ and critical points of I are weak solutions of (2.9). In Appendix B (Proposition B.10), we prove that when (p_1) and (p_2) are satisfied, $I \in C^1(E, \mathbf{R})$ and

$$I'(u)\varphi = \int_\Omega (\nabla u \cdot \nabla \varphi - p(x, u)\varphi)\, dx, \tag{2.12}$$

thereby verifying these two properties.

For our first application, we further assume

(p_3) $p(x, \xi) = o(|\xi|)$ as $\xi \to 0$, and

(p_4) there are constants $\mu > 2$ and $r \geq 0$ such that for $|\xi| \geq r$,

$$0 < \mu P(x, \xi) \leq \xi p(x, \xi).$$

REMARKS 2.13. (i) Hypothesis (p_3) implies that (2.9) possesses the "trivial solution" $u \equiv 0$.

(ii) Integrating condition (p_4) shows that there exist constants $a_3, a_4 > 0$ such that

$$P(x, \xi) \geq a_3|\xi|^\mu - a_4 \tag{2.14}$$

for all $x \in \overline{\Omega}$ and $\xi \in \mathbf{R}^n$. Thus since $\mu > 2$, $P(x,\xi)$ grows at a "superquadratic" rate and by (p_4), p grows at a "superlinear" rate as $|\xi| \to \infty$.

(iii) Note that if $n = 1$ and $p(x,\xi) = \xi^3$, i.e. if we are in the setting of example (1.5), (p_1)–(p_4) are satisfied.

THEOREM 2.15. *If p satisfies (p_1)–(p_4), (2.9) possesses a nontrivial weak solution.*

PROOF. Let $E = W_0^{1,2}(\Omega)$ and I be defined by (2.10). The weak solution I of (2.9) will be obtained as a critical point of I with the aid of Theorem 2.2. Proposition B.10 and (p_1)–(p_2) imply $I \in C^1(E,\mathbf{R})$. Clearly $I(0) = 0$. Thus we must show I satisfies (I_1), (I_2), and (PS). To verify (I_2), note that by (p_4) and (2.14),

$$J(u) \equiv \int_\Omega P(x,u)\,dx \geq a_3 \int_\Omega |u|^\mu\,dx - a_4|\Omega| \tag{2.16}$$

for all $u \in E$, where $|\Omega|$ denotes the measure of Ω. Chosing any $u \in E \setminus \{0\}$, (2.16) implies

$$\begin{aligned} I(tu) &= \frac{t^2}{2}\int_\Omega |\nabla u|^2\,dx - \int_\Omega P(x,tu)\,dx \\ &\leq \frac{t^2}{2}\|u\|^2 - t^\mu a_3 \int_\Omega |u|^\mu\,dx + a_4|\Omega| \to -\infty \end{aligned} \tag{2.17}$$

as $t \to \infty$. Hence (I_2) holds. For (I_1), by (p_3), given any $\varepsilon > 0$, there is a $\delta > 0$ such that $|\xi| \leq \delta$ implies

$$|P(x,\xi)| \leq \tfrac{1}{2}\varepsilon|\xi|^2$$

for all $x \in \overline{\Omega}$. By (p_2) there is a constant $A = A(\delta) > 0$ such that $|\xi| \geq \delta$ implies

$$|P(x,\xi)| \leq A|\xi|^{s+1}$$

for all $x \in \overline{\Omega}$. Combining these two estimates, for all $\xi \in \mathbf{R}$ and $x \in \overline{\Omega}$,

$$|P(x,\xi)| \leq \frac{\varepsilon}{2}|\xi|^2 + A|\xi|^{s+1}. \tag{2.18}$$

Consequently,

$$|J(u)| \leq \frac{\varepsilon}{2}\int_\Omega u^2\,dx + A\int_\Omega |u|^{s+1}\,dx \leq a_5\left(\frac{\varepsilon}{2} + A\|u\|^{s-1}\right)\|u\|^2 \tag{2.19}$$

via the Poincaré and Sobolev inequalities. Choosing $\|u\| \leq (\varepsilon/2A)^{1/(s-1)}$ yields

$$|J(u)| \leq a_5\varepsilon\|u\|^2. \tag{2.20}$$

Since ε was arbitrary, (2.20) shows $J(u) = o(\|u\|^2)$ as $u \to 0$. Therefore

$$I(u) = \tfrac{1}{2}\|u\|^2 - J(u) = \tfrac{1}{2}\|u\|^2 + o(\|u\|^2)$$

as $u \to 0$ so (I_1) holds.

Next the verification of (PS) here and in later results is simplified with the aid of the following result whose proof can be found in Appendix B.

PROPOSITION B.35. *Let p satisfy (p_1)–(p_2) and I be defined by* (2.10). *If (u_m) is a bounded sequence in E such that $I'(u_m) \to 0$ as $m \to \infty$, then (u_m) is precompact in E.*

By Proposition B.35, to verify (PS), we need only show $|I(u_m)| \leq M$ and $I'(u_m) \to 0$ as $m \to \infty$ implies (u_m) is a bounded sequence. For m large, (2.12) with $u = u_m$ and $T = \mu^{-1}p(x,u)u - P(x,u)$ shows

(2.21)

$$M + \mu^{-1}\|u\| \geq I(u) - \mu^{-1}I'(u)u - \left(\frac{1}{2} - \frac{1}{\mu}\right)\|u\|^2 + \int_\Omega T\,dx$$
$$\geq \left(\frac{1}{2} - \frac{1}{\mu}\right)\|u\|^2 + \int_{\{x\in\Omega|\,|u(x)|\geq r\}} T\,dx + \int_{\{x\in\Omega|\,|u(x)|<r\}} T\,dx.$$

By (p_4), $(2^{-1} - \mu^{-1}) > 0$ and the second term on the right in (2.21) is positive. The third term is bounded by a constant independently of m. Hence (2.21) implies (u_m) is bounded in E.

Lastly note that $I(0) = 0$ while for our critical point u, $I(u) \geq \alpha > 0$. Hence u is a nontrivial weak solution of (2.9).

REMARK 2.22. If hypothesis (p_1) is strengthened to, e.g.,

(p_1') $p(x,\xi)$ is locally Lipschitz continuous in $\overline{\Omega} \times \mathbf{R}$,

then (p_1')–(p_2) imply any weak solution of (2.9) in E is a classical solution of (2.9) (see e.g. [**Ag**]).

COROLLARY 2.23. *Under the hypothesis of Theorem* 2.15, *if p also satisfies (p_1'), then* (2.9) *possesses a positive and a negative classical solution.*

PROOF. Set $\overline{p}(x,\xi) = 0$ for $\xi \leq 0$ and $\overline{p}(x,\xi) = p(x,\xi)$ for $\xi \geq 0$. Let

$$\overline{P}(x,\xi) = \int_0^\xi \overline{p}(x,t)\,dt.$$

The arguments of Theorem 2.15 show that

$$\overline{I}(u) = \tfrac{1}{2}\|u\|^2 - \int_\Omega \overline{P}(x,u)\,dx \tag{2.24}$$

satisfy the hypotheses of the Mountain Pass Theorem. Indeed $\overline{p}$ satisfies (p_1)–(p_3). Moreover, (p_4) holds for $\xi > 0$ while $0 = \overline{P} = \overline{p}$ for $\xi \leq 0$. Hypothesis (p_4) was required to help verify (PS) and (I_2). The above weaker version of (p_4) implies $\overline{P} \geq \mu^{-1}\overline{p}$ for large $|\xi|$ and this suffices to get (PS). To also satisfy (I_2), note that (2.14) holds for $\xi \geq 0$. Thus choosing $u \in E \setminus \{0\}$ in (2.17) to be a nonnegative function, (I_2) holds. Consequently, by the Mountain Pass Theorem

$$\begin{aligned} -\Delta u &= \overline{p}(x,u), \qquad x \in \Omega, \\ u &= 0, \qquad x \in \partial\Omega, \end{aligned} \tag{2.25}$$

has a weak solution, $u \not\equiv 0$. By (p_1') and Remark 2.22, u is a classical solution of (2.25). Let $\mathcal{A} = \{x \in \Omega | u(x) < 0\}$. Then by the definition of $\overline{p}$,

$$\begin{aligned} -\Delta u &= 0, \qquad x \in \mathcal{A}, \\ u &= 0, \qquad x \in \partial\mathcal{A}. \end{aligned}$$

Consequently the maximum principle shows $u \equiv 0$ in $\mathcal{A}$ so $\mathcal{A} = \emptyset$. Thus $u \geq 0$ in Ω. In fact rewriting (2.25) as

$$
\begin{aligned}
-\Delta u - \left(\frac{\overline{p}(x,u)^-}{u}\right) u &= \left(\frac{\overline{p}(x,u)^+}{u}\right) u, \qquad x \in \Omega, \\
u = 0, &\qquad x \in \partial\Omega,
\end{aligned}
\tag{2.26}
$$

where $a^+ = \max(a,0)$ and $a^- = \min(a,0)$, and noting that $\xi^{-1}\overline{p}(x,\xi)^{\pm}$ are continuous if defined to be 0 at $\xi = 0$, the strong maximum principle [**CH**] implies that $u(x) > 0$ for $x \in \Omega$ and $\partial u(x)/\partial\nu < 0$ for $x \in \partial\Omega$, $\nu(x)$ being the outward pointing normal to $\partial\Omega$ at x.

The negative solution of (2.9) is produced in a similar fashion.

REMARK 2.27. Theorem 2.15 and Corollary 2.23 can be found in [**AR**]. Earlier work in this direction was done by Coffman [**Co1–2**] and Hempel [**He1**].

REMARK 2.28. If $p = p(\xi)$ and $n > 2$, an identity due to Pohozaev [**Po**] says

$$
\int_\Omega (2nP(u) + (2-n)up(u))\,dx = \int_{\partial\Omega} x \cdot \nu(x)|\nabla u|^2\,dS \tag{2.29}
$$

for all solutions of (2.9).
Consequently if Ω is starshaped with respect to the origin, i.e. $x \cdot \nu(x) \geq 0$ for all $x \in \partial\Omega$, then

$$
\int_\Omega P(u)\,dx \geq \frac{n-2}{2n}\int_\Omega up(u)\,dx. \tag{2.30}
$$

By imposing additional conditions, e.g. $x \cdot \nu(x) \not\equiv 0$ and $u > 0$ in Ω so $\nabla u \neq 0$ on $\partial\Omega$, the inequality in (2.30) becomes strict. Taking in particular $P^*(\xi) = (s+1)^{-1}|\xi|^{s+1}$ then shows $s < (n+2)(n-2)^{-1}$ is a necessary condition for there to exist solutions of (2.9). On the other hand, Brezis and Nirenberg [**BN**] have established some existence results for $P(\xi) = P^*(\xi)+$ lower order term when s equals the limit exponent $(n+2)(n-2)^{-1}$. In work in progress, Bahri and Coron have shown if $n = 3$, and $P(\xi) = P^*(\xi)$ with s the limit exponent and Ω noncontractible, then (2.9) has a positive solution. If Ω is an annulus in $\mathbf{R}^n$ it is also known that there exists a positive solution of (2.9) for $P(\xi) = P^*(\xi)$ for all values of s. Just what the relationship between the geometry of Ω and growth conditions on p need be for there to exist solutions of (2.9) remains an interesting open question.

Our next application concerns a nonlinear eigenvalue problem

$$
\begin{aligned}
-\Delta u = \lambda p(u), &\qquad x \in \Omega, \\
u = 0, &\qquad x \in \partial\Omega,
\end{aligned}
\tag{2.31}
$$

where $\lambda \in \mathbf{R}$. For a class of such problems, $\xi^2 - \xi^3$ being a good model case, we will show (2.31) has at least *two* positive solutions for all large λ.

THEOREM 2.32 [**AR**]. *Suppose p satisfies (p_1'), (p_2) and*
(p_5) there is an $r > 0$ such that $p(\xi) > 0$ for $\xi \in (0,r)$ and $p(r) = 0$.

Then there exists a $\underline{\lambda} > 0$ *such that for all* $\lambda > \underline{\lambda}$, (2.31) *has at least two classical solutions* ***which*** *are positive in* Ω.

PROOF. As with Corollary 2.23, the proof begins by redefining p. Set $\overline{p}(\xi) = p(\xi)$ for $\xi \in [0, r]$ and $\overline{p}(\xi) = 0$ otherwise. Then $\overline{p}$ satisfies $(p_1'), (p_2), (p_3)$, and (p_5). If u is a solution of

$$\text{(2.33)} \qquad \begin{aligned} -\Delta u &= \lambda \overline{p}(u), \qquad x \in \Omega, \\ u &= 0, \qquad x \in \partial\Omega, \end{aligned}$$

the argument of Corollary 2.23 shows $\{x \in \Omega | u < 0\} = \varnothing$ and $u > 0$ in Ω. Similar reasoning proves $\{x \in \Omega | u(x) > r\} = \varnothing$. Hence $0 < u(x) \leq r$ in Ω so u satisfies (2.31). By these observations and Remark 2.22, to find solutions of (2.31), it suffices to produce nontrivial critical points of

$$\text{(2.34)} \qquad I_\lambda(u) \equiv \tfrac{1}{2}\|u\|^2 - \lambda \int_\Omega \overline{P}(u)\, dx$$

on $E = W_0^{1,2}(\Omega)$, $\overline{P}$ being the primitive of $\overline{p}$.

To study the properties of I_λ, note first that since $\overline{p}$ satisfies (p_1)–(p_2), $I_\lambda \in C^1(E, \mathbf{R})$. Moreover (PS) holds for I_λ: if (u_m) is a sequence in E with $I_\lambda(u_m) \leq M$, the boundedness of $\overline{p}$ implies $|\overline{P}(\xi)| \leq a_6|\xi|$ and

$$\text{(2.35)} \qquad M \geq I_\lambda(u_m) \geq \tfrac{1}{2}\|u_m\|^2 - |\lambda| a_6 \int_\Omega |u_m|\, dx.$$

Applying the Hölder and Poincaré inequalities, (2.35) shows (u_m) is bounded in E. Hence (PS) follows from Proposition B.35. Note that (2.35) also implies $I_\lambda(u)$ is bounded from below. Hence by Theorem 2.7,

$$\text{(2.36)} \qquad b_\lambda \equiv \inf_E I_\lambda(u)$$

is a critical value of I_λ for all $\lambda \in \mathbf{R}$. It may be the case that $b_\lambda = 0$ corresponding to the trivial critical point $u = 0$ of I_λ. Indeed (p_2)–(p_3) and the arguments centered around (2.18)–(2.19) show $u = 0$ is a local minimum of I_λ and I_λ satisfies (I_1). In fact

$$\text{(2.37)} \qquad I_\lambda(u) \geq \tfrac{1}{4}\|u\|^2$$

for $|\lambda| \leq \lambda_0$ and $\|u\| \leq a_7$ provided that λ_0 and a_7 are sufficiently small. On the other hand as in (2.35) the linear growth of $\overline{P}$ in ξ implies

$$\text{(2.38)} \qquad I_\lambda(u) \geq \tfrac{1}{2}\|u\|^2 - |\lambda| a_8 \|u\|$$

for all $\lambda \in \mathbf{R}$ and $u \in E$. Thus for small λ (2.37)–(2.38) show $I_\lambda(u) \geq 0 = I_\lambda(0)$. Consequently $b_\lambda = 0$.

To obtain a nontrivial solution, let $\varphi \in E \setminus \{0\}$ such that $\varphi(x) \in [0, r)$ for $x \in \Omega$. By (p_5)

$$\int_\Omega P(\varphi(x))\, dx > 0.$$

Thus for λ sufficiently large, $I_\lambda(\varphi) < 0$ and $b_\lambda < 0$. Define $\underline{\lambda} \equiv \inf\{\lambda > 0 | b_\lambda < 0\}$. Then for all $\lambda > \underline{\lambda}$, the above remarks show I_λ has a criticial value $b_\lambda < 0$ and a corresponding critical point $\underline{u}_\lambda$ which is a positive solution of (2.33). Moreover since $I_\lambda(\underline{u}_\lambda) < 0$, I_λ satisfies (I_2) of Theorem 2.2. Consequently the Mountain Pass Theorem yields a second critical point $\overline{u}_\lambda$ of I_λ such that $I_\lambda(\overline{u}_\lambda) > 0 > I_\lambda(\underline{u}_\lambda)$. Clearly $\overline{u}_\lambda$ is distinct from $\underline{u}_\lambda$ and again by above remarks is a positive solution of (2.33). The proof is complete.

Our final application in this section is to a problem for which one can establish the existence of at least three nontrivial solutions. Consider the equation:

$$\begin{aligned} -\Delta u &= \lambda a(x)u - p(x,u), \qquad x \in \Omega, \\ u &= 0, \qquad x \in \partial\Omega. \end{aligned} \tag{2.39}$$

The function a is assumed to be positive and e.g. Lipschitz continuous in $\overline{\Omega}$. Associated with (2.39) is the Sturm-Liouville eigenvalue problem:

$$\begin{aligned} -\Delta v &= \mu a(x)v, \qquad x \in \Omega, \\ v &= 0, \qquad x \in \partial\Omega. \end{aligned} \tag{2.40}$$

As is well known, (2.40) possesses a sequence of eigenvalues (λ_j) with $0 < \lambda_1 < \lambda_2 \le \cdots \le \lambda_j \le \cdots$ and $\lambda_j \to \infty$ as $j \to \infty$. (The number of times an eigenvalue appears in the sequence equals its multiplicity.)

Concerning solutions of (2.39) we have

PROPOSITION 2.41. *Suppose p satisfies (p_3) and*
(p_6) (i) $0 < h(x,\xi) \equiv p(x,\xi)\xi^{-1}$ *for* $\xi \ne 0$,
(ii) $h \in C^1(\overline{\Omega} \times \mathbf{R}, \mathbf{R})$ *and* $\xi h_\xi(x,\xi) > 0$ *for* $\xi \ne 0$,
(iii) $h(x,\xi) \to \infty$ *as* $|\xi| \to \infty$ *uniformly for* $x \in \overline{\Omega}$.
Then: $(1°)$ *for* $\lambda \le \lambda_1$, (2.39) *possesses only the trivial solution* $u \equiv 0$. $(2°)$ *For each* $\lambda > \lambda_1$, (2.39) *possesses a pair of solutions* u_λ^+, u_λ^- *with* u_λ^+ (*resp.* u_λ^-) *the unique solution of* (2.39) *with* $u_\lambda^+ > 0$ *in* Ω (*resp.* $u_\lambda^- < 0$ *in* Ω). *In fact the maps* $\lambda \to u_\lambda^\pm$ *are* C^1 *for* $\lambda > \lambda_1$ *and* $u_\lambda^\pm \to 0$ *as* $\lambda \to \lambda_1$.

Since p satisfies (p_3), $u \equiv 0$ is a solution of (2.39) for any value of λ. The first assertion of Proposition 2.41 follows simply on multiplying (2.39) by u, integrating by parts, and using (p_6)(i). The second statement can be proved in a variety of different ways—see e.g. [**R1**, **St2**]—and will be omitted here. We will prove the following result which is essentially due to Struwe [**St2**].

THEOREM 2.42. *If p satisfies (p_3) and (p_6), then for all $\lambda > \lambda_2$, (2.39) possesses at least three nontrivial solutions.*

The proof of Theorem 2.42 will be carried out in a series of steps. First observe that (p_6)(iii) implies an a priori bound for solutions of (2.39). Indeed if u is a nontrivial solution, either u has a positive (global) maximum or a negative minimum. Assuming the former, if the max is attained at $z \in \Omega$,

$$0 \le -\Delta u(z) = \lambda a(z)u(z) - p(x,z)$$

or

$$h(z,u(z)) \le \lambda a(z). \tag{2.43}$$

The same inequality holds at a negative minimum. Hence by (p_6)(iii), there is a constant $M = M(\lambda) > 0$ such that $\|u\|_{L^\infty} \le M(\lambda)$. In fact since λ is fixed, choosing $\overline{\lambda} > \lambda$ there is an $\overline{M}$ depending on $\overline{\lambda}$ such that $\|u\|_{L^\infty} \le \overline{M}$ for any solution of (2.39) with $\lambda \le \overline{\lambda}$. With this observation, $p(x,\xi)$ or actually $h(x,\xi)$ can be modified for $|\xi| \ge \overline{M}$ as in Corollary 2.23 or Theorem 2.32, so that hypotheses (p_6)(i)–(iii) also hold for the modification $\overline{p}(x,\xi) = \xi\overline{h}(x,\xi)$ and $\overline{p}$ satisfies

$(\overline{p}_2)$ $|\overline{p}(x,\xi)| \le \overline{a}_1 + \overline{a}_2|\xi|^{s-1}$

for some s as in (p_2). Moreover solutions of

$$\begin{aligned} -\Delta u &= \lambda a u - \overline{p}(x,u), \qquad x \in \Omega,\\ u &= 0, \qquad x \in \partial\Omega, \end{aligned} \tag{2.44}$$

for $\lambda \le \overline{\lambda}$ are also solutions of (2.39).

It remains to find a third nontrivial solution of (2.44). As usual let $E = W_0^{1,2}(\Omega)$ and define

$$I_\lambda(u) = \int_\Omega \left[\frac{1}{2}|\nabla u|^2 - \frac{\lambda}{2}au^2 - \overline{P}(x,u)\right] dx,$$

where $\overline{P}$ is the primitive of $\overline{p}$. Since (p_6)(ii) implies $(\hat{p}_1)$ of Proposition B.34 for $\overline{p}$ and $(\overline{p}_2)$ implies $(\hat{p}_2)$, by that result, $I_\lambda \in C^2(E,\mathbf{R})$. Moreover I_λ satisfies (PS) for, suppose

$$K \ge I_\lambda(u_m) = \frac{1}{2}\|u_m\|^2 - \frac{\lambda}{2}\int_\Omega au_m^2\,dx + \int_\Omega \overline{P}(x,u_m)\,dx. \tag{2.45}$$

By (p_6)(iii), for any $\beta > 0$ there is a $\gamma = \gamma(\beta) \ge 0$ such that for all $x \in \overline{\Omega}$ and $\xi \in \mathbf{R}$,

$$\overline{P}(x,\xi) \ge \beta\xi^2 - \gamma. \tag{2.46}$$

Choosing $\beta > \lambda\|a\|_{L^\infty}/2$, (2.45)–(2.46) show (u_m) is bounded in E so (PS) follows from Proposition B.35.

We want to find a critical point u_λ of I_λ other than the known ones 0, $u_\lambda^\pm$ given by Proposition 2.41. Concerning the latter we have:

LEMMA 2.47. *If $\lambda > \lambda_1$, then $I_\lambda(u_\lambda^\pm) < 0$ and $u_\lambda^\pm$ are strict local minima of I_λ.*

PROOF. The map $\lambda \to u_\lambda^\pm$ is C^1 for $\lambda > \lambda_1$. Hence

$$\frac{d}{d\lambda}I_\lambda(u_\lambda^\pm) = I_\lambda'(u_\lambda^\pm)\frac{\partial u_\lambda^\pm}{\partial\lambda} - \frac{1}{2}\int_\Omega a(u_\lambda^\pm)^2\,dx < 0$$

since $I_\lambda'(u_\lambda^\pm) = 0$. Moreover by Proposition 2.41, $u_\lambda^\pm \to 0$ as $\lambda \to \lambda_1$ and $I_\lambda(0) = 0$. Hence $I_\lambda(u_\lambda^\pm) < 0$ for $\lambda > \lambda_1$.

To show that $u_\lambda^\pm$ are strict local minima of I_λ, we will use a comparison argument. Let $w = u_\lambda^+$ or u_λ^-. Since $I_\lambda \in C^2(E, \mathbf{R})$, for u near w,

$$I_\lambda(u) = I_\lambda(w) + I_\lambda'(w)(u-w) + \tfrac{1}{2}I_\lambda''(w)(u-w, u-w) + o(\|u-w\|^2). \tag{2.48}$$

Since $I_\lambda'(w) = 0$, to show w is a strict local minimum for I_λ, by (2.48) and Proposition B.34, it suffices to show that

$$I_\lambda''(w)(\varphi,\varphi) = \int_\Omega [|\nabla\varphi|^2 - \lambda a\varphi^2 + (h(x,w) + wh_u(x,w))\varphi^2]\,dx \geq \beta\|\varphi\|^2 \tag{2.49}$$

for some $\beta > 0$ and all $\varphi \in E$. The eigenvalue problem

$$\begin{aligned} -\Delta v + h(x,w)v &= \mu a v, \qquad x \in \Omega, \\ v &= 0, \qquad x \in \partial\Omega, \end{aligned} \tag{2.50}$$

has as a solution $\mu = \lambda$ and $v = w$ with v of one sign in Ω. Hence λ must be the smallest eigenvalue to (2.50). Moreover λ can be characterized as [**CH**]:

$$\lambda = \inf_{0 \neq v \in E} \frac{\int_\Omega (|\nabla v|^2 + h(x,w)v^2)\,dx}{\int_\Omega a v^2\,dx}. \tag{2.51}$$

Comparing (2.51) to

$$\gamma \equiv \inf_{0 \neq v \in E} \frac{\int_\Omega [|\nabla u|^2 + (h(x,w) + wh_u(x,w))v^2]\,dx}{\int_\Omega a v^2\,dx}, \tag{2.52}$$

(p_6)(ii) shows that $\gamma > \lambda$. This fact and (2.52) then show

$$\begin{aligned} I_\lambda''(w)(\varphi,\varphi) &\geq \left(1 - \frac{\lambda}{\gamma}\right)\int_\Omega [|\nabla\varphi|^2 + (h(x,w) + wh_u(x,w))\varphi^2]\,dx \\ &\geq \left(1 - \frac{\lambda}{\gamma}\right)\|\varphi\|^2 \end{aligned} \tag{2.53}$$

and the lemma is proved.

With the aid of Lemma 2.47, we will find another critical point of I_λ. Consider the larger of $I_\lambda(u_\lambda^\pm)$. (If these numbers are equal either will suffice.) Suppose it occurs at u_λ^+. Making the change of variables $U = u - u_\lambda^+$ and setting $\Phi_\lambda(U) = I_\lambda(U + u_\lambda^+) - I_\lambda(u_\lambda^+)$, we see that $\Phi_\lambda \in C^1(E, \mathbf{R})$, $\Phi_\lambda(0) = 0$, and Φ_λ satisfies (PS). Moreover Lemma 2.47 and our choice of origin show I_λ satisfies (I_1) and (I_2) since $I_\lambda(u_\lambda^+) \geq I_\lambda(u_\lambda^-)$. Thus the Mountain Pass Theorem shows I_λ has a positive critical value. Returning to the original coordinate system, it follows that I_λ has a critical value $c_\lambda > I_\lambda(u_\lambda^+)$, where

$$c_\lambda = \inf_{g \in \Gamma_\lambda} \max_{t \in [0,1]} I_\lambda(g(t))$$

and

$$\Gamma_\lambda = \{g \in C([0,1], E) | g(0) = u_\lambda^+, g(1) = u_\lambda^-\}.$$

Since $I_\lambda(0) = 0 > I_\lambda(u_\lambda^+)$ by Lemma 2.47 and 0 is a critical point of I_λ, a priori it may be the case that $c_\lambda = 0$ and the corresponding critical point is $u_\lambda \equiv 0$. Thus to ensure that u_λ is nontrivial it suffices to show that $c_\lambda < 0$. To do this, the fact that $\lambda > \lambda_2$ will be used. We will construct a curve $g_\lambda \in \Gamma_\lambda$ such that I_λ is strictly negative on $g_\lambda([0,1])$. Before doing so, some further observations about I_λ are needed.

Note first that

$$I_\lambda(tu) \le t^2 I_\lambda(u) \tag{2.54}$$

for all $u \in E$ and $t \in [0,1]$. Indeed by (p_6)(ii)

$$\begin{aligned} \overline{P}(x,tz) &= \int_0^{tz} \overline{p}(x,\xi)\,d\xi = \int_0^z \overline{p}(x,ty)t\,dy \\ &= t^2\int_0^z h(x,ty)y\,dy \le t^2\int_0^z h(x,y)y\,dy = t^2\overline{P}(x,z) \end{aligned} \tag{2.55}$$

for any $t \in [0,1]$ and $z \in \mathbf{R}$. Therefore

$$I_\lambda(tu) = t^2\int_\Omega \tfrac{1}{2}(|\nabla u|^2 - \lambda a u^2)\,dx + \int_\Omega \overline{P}(x,tu)\,dx \le t^2 I_\lambda(u) \tag{2.56}$$

for all $u \in E$.

Next let V denote the span of all eigenfunctions of (2.40) corresponding to λ_1 and λ_2 and let W denote the closure (in E) of the span of the remaining eigenvectors of (2.40). Thus $E = V \oplus W$ and it is easy to check that

$$\left(-\int_\Omega(|\nabla v|^2 - \lambda a v^2)\,dx\right)^{1/2}, \quad \left(\int_\Omega |\nabla w|^2 - \lambda a w^2\right)^{1/2}$$

can be taken as equivalent norms on V and W. Abusing notation somewhat, we will write $\|v\|, \|w\|$ for these norms. Thus for $u = v + w \in E$,

$$I_\lambda(u) = -\tfrac{1}{2}\|v\|^2 + \tfrac{1}{2}\|w\|^2 + \int_\Omega \overline{P}(x, v+w)\,dx. \tag{2.57}$$

If $I_\lambda(u) < 0$, (2.57) and (p_6)(i) show

$$\|v\|^2 > \|w\|^2 + 2\int_\Omega \overline{P}(x,v+w)\,dx > \|w\|^2. \tag{2.58}$$

Therefore there exists a $\delta = \delta(u) > 0$ such that

$$\|v\| > (1+\delta)\|w\|. \tag{2.59}$$

Set $u_\lambda^\pm = v_\lambda^\pm + w_\lambda^\pm$. Since $I_\lambda(u_\lambda^\pm) < 0$, (2.59) shows $\|v_\lambda^\pm\| > 0$.

Now the path $g_\lambda \in \Gamma_\lambda$ can be constructed. The path consists of five parts:

(a$^+$) The first part is the line segment $\{tu_\lambda^+ | t \in [\tau^+, 1]\}$, where $\tau^+\|v_\lambda^+\| = \rho$ and $\rho > 0$ is free for the moment. It is clear from (2.56) that $I_\lambda < 0$ on this segment

(b$^+$) Homotopy $\tau^+ u_\lambda^+$ to $\tau^+ v_\lambda^+$ via $\tau^+(v_\lambda^+ + \theta w_\lambda^+)$.

(c) Join $\tau^+ v_\lambda^+$ to $\tau^- v_\lambda^-$ on $\partial B_\rho \cap V$, where $\tau^-\|v_\lambda^-\| = \rho$. Note that $\partial B_\rho \cap V$ is a connected set since $\lambda > \lambda_2$ implies the dimension of V is at least 2.

(b$^-$) Homotopy $\tau^- v_\lambda^-$ to $\tau^- u_\lambda^-$ as in (b$^+$).

(a$^-$) Join $\tau^- u_\lambda^-$ to u_λ^- by a straight line segment. As in (a$^+$), here $I_\lambda < 0$.

To complete the proof, we must show $I_\lambda < 0$ for steps ($\mathrm{b}^\pm$) and (c) if ρ is sufficiently small. For $\theta \in [0,1]$,

$$I_\lambda(\tau^\pm(v_\lambda^\pm + \theta w_\lambda^\pm)) = -\frac{1}{2}\rho^2 + \frac{\theta^2(\tau^\pm)^2}{2}\|w_\lambda^\pm\|^2 + \int_\Omega \overline{P}(x, \tau^\pm(v_\lambda^\pm + \theta w_\lambda^\pm))\,dx. \tag{2.60}$$

Hence by (2.55), (2.59) with $\delta_1 = \min(\delta(u_\lambda^+), \delta(u_\lambda^-))$, and some simple estimates,

$$I_\lambda(\tau^\pm(v_\lambda^\pm + \theta w_\lambda^\pm)) \le \rho^2\left(-\frac{1}{2} + \frac{\theta^2}{2(1+\delta_1)^2} + o(1)\right) \le \text{const} < 0 \tag{2.61}$$

as $\rho \to 0$. Hence $I_\lambda < 0$ for ($\mathrm{b}^\pm$). A similar estimate shows $I_\lambda < 0$ for (c) and the proof of Theorem 2.42 is complete.

REMARK 2.62. For some related applications of the Mountain Pass Theorem see [**CR**, **G**].

3. Some Variants of the Mountain Pass Theorem

In this brief section we will examine some other versions of the Mountain Pass Theorem as well as some small generalizations. In Theorem 2.2, the critical value c was obtained by minimaxing I over all curves which join 0 and e. This choice of sets is rather arbitrary. There are several other natural classes of sets with which one can work. E.g. set

$$\Gamma_0 = \{g([0,1])|g \text{ is 1-1}, g(0) = 0, g(1) = e\},$$
$$\Gamma_1 = \{K \subset E|K \text{ is compact, connected, and } 0, e \in K\},$$

and

$$\Gamma_2 = \{K \subset E|K \text{ is closed, connected, and } 0, e \in K\}.$$

Define

$$c_i = \inf_{K \in \Gamma_i} \sup_{u \in K} I(u), \qquad i = 0, 1, 2.$$

Since $\Gamma_0 \subset \{g([0,1])|g \in \Gamma\} \subset \Gamma_1 \subset \Gamma_2$, it follows that $c_0 \geq c \geq c_1 \geq c_2$. Moreover the proof of Theorem 2.2 shows that c_1 is a critical value of I. Noting that by Theorem A.4, $\eta(1,\cdot)$ is homeomorphism of E onto E, it follows that $\eta(1,\cdot)\colon \Gamma_i \to \Gamma_i$, $i = 0, 2$. With this additional observation the proof of Theorem 2.2 also shows c_0 and c_2 are critical values of I.

What is the relationship between these numbers? It is not difficult to see that if $K \in \Gamma_1$ and $\varepsilon > 0$, there is a $g([0,1]) \in \Gamma_0$ such that K lies in a uniform ε-neighborhood of $g([0,1])$. Thus $c_0 = c = c_1$. We do not know if c_2 can differ from this common value.

Remaining in the setting of Theorem 2.2 there are other ways in which critical values of I can be characterized that are "dual" in a sense to those that we have just seen. E.g. let

$$W \equiv \{B \subset E|B \text{ is open}, 0 \in B, \text{ and } e \notin \overline{B}\}. \tag{3.1}$$

THEOREM 3.2 [**AR**]. *Let I satisfy the hypotheses of Theorem 2.2. Then*

$$b \equiv \sup_{B \in W} \inf_{u \in \partial B} I(u) \tag{3.3}$$

is a critical value of I with $\alpha \leq b \leq c$.

PROOF. By (I_1), $B_\rho \in W$. Therefore (3.3) implies $b \geq \alpha$. If $g \in \Gamma$ and $B \in W$, there is a $w \in g([0,1]) \cap \partial B$. Hence

$$\inf_{\partial B} I \leq I(w) \leq \max_{t\in[0,1]} I(g(t)). \tag{3.4}$$

Since g and B are arbitrary, (3.4) implies that $b \leq c$. Lastly suppose that b is not a critical value of I. Then by (the Deformation) Theorem A.4 (with $\overline{\varepsilon} = \alpha/2$) and Remark A.7(ii), there is an $\varepsilon \in (0, \overline{\varepsilon})$ and $\hat{\eta} \in C([0,1] \times E, E)$ such that

$$\hat{\eta}(1, \hat{A}_{b-\varepsilon}) \subset \hat{A}_{b+\varepsilon}, \tag{3.5}$$

where $\hat{A}_s = \{u \in E | I(u) \geq s\}$. Choose $B \in W$ such that

$$\inf_{\partial B} I \geq b - \varepsilon. \tag{3.6}$$

By 3° of Theorem A.4, $\hat{\eta}(1, \cdot)$ is a homeomorphism of E onto E. Therefore $\hat{\eta}(1, B)$ is an open set. Our choice of $\overline{\varepsilon}$ and 2° of Theorem A.4 imply $\hat{\eta}(1,0) = 0$ and $\hat{\eta}(1,e) = e$. Hence $0 \in \hat{\eta}(1,B)$ and $e \notin \overline{\hat{\eta}(1,B)} = \hat{\eta}(1,\overline{B})$. Consequently $\hat{\eta}(1,B) \in W$ with $\partial\hat{\eta}(1,B) = \hat{\eta}(1,\partial B)$. Thus by (3.5)–(3.6) and the definition of b,

$$b + \varepsilon \leq \inf_{\partial(\hat{\eta}(1,B))} I \leq b, \tag{3.7}$$

a contradiction.

REMARK 3.8. Simple examples for $E = \mathbf{R}^n$ or even $\mathbf{R}$ show that b may be less than c.

REMARK 3.9. The class of sets W of Theorem 3.2 is "dual" to classes introduced earlier in that $B \in W$ implies that $B \cap K \neq \varnothing$ for all $K \in \Gamma_0, \Gamma_1$, etc. Define

$$W_1 = \{h(\partial B_\rho) | h \text{ is a homeomorphism of } E \text{ onto } E \text{ and } h(0) = 0, h(e) = e\}$$

and

$$W_2 = \{K \in E | K \cap g([0,1]) \neq \varnothing \text{ for each } g \in \Gamma\}.$$

Thus $W_2 \supset \{\partial B | B \in W\} \supset W_1$. Therefore if

$$b_i = \sup_{K\in W_i} \inf_{u\in K} I(u), \qquad i = 1,2,$$

then $c \geq b_2 \geq b \geq b_1$ and it is not difficult to show that b_1 and b_2 are critical values of I. In fact $b_2 = c$ since for each $g \in \Gamma$, there is a $\xi = \xi(g) \in E$ such that

$$\max_{g([0,1])} I = I(\xi).$$

Set $K = \bigcup_{g\in\Gamma} \xi(g)$. Then $K \cap g([0,1]) \neq \varnothing$ for each $g \in \Gamma$. Therefore $K \in W_2$ and $\inf_K I = c$.

The next result generalizes Theorem 2.2 by weakening (I_1). W refers to (3.1).

THEOREM 3.10. *Let $I \in C^1(E, \mathbf{R})$ and satisfy (PS). Suppose that*
(I_1^*) $I(0) = 0$ *and there is a* $B \in W$ *such that* $I|_{\partial B} \geq 0$, *and*
(I_2^*) *there is an* $e \in E \setminus \overline{B}$ *such that* $I(e) \leq 0$
hold. Then b defined in (3.3) is a critical value of I with $b \geq 0$. If $b = 0$, there exists a critical value of I on ∂B.

PROOF. If $b > 0$, the proof of Theorem 3.2 with e.g. $\overline{\varepsilon} = b/2$ carries over to the present situation. Thus suppose $b = 0$. Since $0 \in B$ and $e \notin \overline{B}$, without loss of generality we can assume

$$\min(\mathrm{dist}(e, \overline{B}), \mathrm{dist}(0, \partial B)) > 1, \tag{3.11}$$

where $\mathrm{dist}(X, Y)$ refers to the distance between sets X and Y. Suppose that I has no critical value on ∂B, i.e. $I' \neq 0$ on ∂B. Since the set of critical points K_0 is compact, there exists a neighborhood, $\mathcal{O}$, of K_0 such that $\mathcal{O} \cap \partial B = \emptyset$. By Theorem A.4 with e.g. $\overline{\varepsilon} = 1$ and Remark A.17(iii), there is an $\varepsilon \in (0, 1)$ and $\tilde{\eta} \in C([0, 1] \times E, E)$ such that

$$\tilde{\eta}(1, \hat{A}_{-\varepsilon} \setminus \mathcal{O}) \subset \hat{A}_{\varepsilon}. \tag{3.12}$$

In particular by (I_1^*) and our choice of $\mathcal{O}$, $\partial B \subset \hat{A}_{-\varepsilon} \setminus \mathcal{O}$. Therefore by (3.12) and 3° of Theorem A.4, $\tilde{\eta}(1, \partial B) = \partial \tilde{\eta}(1, B) \subset \hat{A}_{\varepsilon}$ and

$$\inf_{\tilde{\eta}(1, \partial B)} I \geq \varepsilon > 0. \tag{3.13}$$

We claim $\tilde{\eta}(1, B) \in W$ and therefore (3.13) contradicts $b = 0$. By 3° of Theorem A.4, there is an $x \in E$ such that $\tilde{\eta}(1, x) = 0$ and by 4° of Theorem A.4,

$$\|\tilde{\eta}(1, x) - x\| = \|x\| \leq 1.$$

Hence by (3.11), $x \in B$ and $\tilde{\eta}(1, B)$ is a neighborhood of 0. Lastly $e \notin \tilde{\eta}(1, B)$. Indeed, again by 3° and 4° of Theorem A.4, there is a $y \in E$ such that $\tilde{\eta}(1, y) = e$ and $\|\tilde{\eta}(1, y) - y\| = \|e - y\| \leq 1$ while if $y \in \overline{B}$, $\|y - e\| > 1$ by (3.11). The proof is complete.

REMARK 3.14. Theorem 3.10 was motivated by work of Pucci and Serrin [**PS**]. The following corollary can also be found in [**PS**].

COROLLARY 3.15. *Let $I \in C^1(E, \mathbf{R})$ and satisfy (PS). If I has a pair of local minima (or maxima), then I possesses a third critical point.*

PROOF. Let u_1, u_2 be the two critical points and suppose $I(u_1) \geq I(u_2)$. Translating variables so that u_1 becomes the origin and replacing $I(u)$ by $I^*(u) = I(u) - I(u_1)$, we see that I^* satisfies the hypotheses of Theorem 3.10 with $e = u_2 - u_1$ and B the boundary of any small neighborhood of 0. Hence I possesses a critical value larger than $I(u_1)$ or equal to $I(u_1)$ in which case I has a critical point on ∂B.

REMARK 3.16. If the third critical value equals $I(u_1)$, then I has a critical point on ∂B for all small neighborhoods B of u_1. An argument from point set topology then shows K_b contains a component of solutions which meets ∂B for all such small B [**Wh**].

REMARK 3.17. In roughly the setting of Theorem 2.2 or 3.10, several authors have studied when any of the corresponding critical points is a "saddle point" of some sort. Taking e.g. $E = \mathbf{R}^n$ and $I(u) = \|u\|^2 - \|u\|^4$ one sees that there need not be any saddle point. However several positive results have been obtained. See e.g. [**Ni, Ho2, PS**].

4. The Saddle Point Theorem

The main goal of this section is to prove the Saddle Point Theorem stated in Chapter 1. The proof requires a simple application of the theory of topological degree in $\mathbf{R}^n$, i.e. *Brouwer degree*. Since degree theory will also be needed in Chapter 5, we will make a brief digression to discuss this subject. A detailed treatment in the spirit of our exposition can be found in [**S2**].

Let $\mathcal{O} \subset \mathbf{R}^n$ be bounded and open, $\varphi \in C^1(\overline{\mathcal{O}}, \mathbf{R}^n)$, and $b \in \mathbf{R}^n \setminus \varphi(\partial \mathcal{O})$. The theory of degree is concerned with the existence and multiplicity of solutions of the equation

$$\varphi(x) = b. \tag{4.1}$$

Suppose $\varphi'(x)$ is nonsingular whenever $\varphi(x) = b$. Then the Inverse Function Theorem shows the solutions of (4.1) are isolated. By hypothesis, $b \notin \varphi(\partial\mathcal{O})$ and $\overline{\mathcal{O}}$ is compact. Hence (4.1) can have only a finite number of solutions in $\mathcal{O}$. For this "nice" case, the (Brouwer) degree of φ with respect to $\mathcal{O}$ and b, denoted by $d(\varphi, \mathcal{O}, b)$, is defined to be

$$d(\varphi, \mathcal{O}, b) = \sum_{x \in \varphi^{-1}(b) \cap \mathcal{O}} \operatorname{sign} \det \varphi'(x), \tag{4.2}$$

where $\det A$ denotes the determinant of a square matrix A.

From this definition it is immediate that for such "nice" φ:

(4.3)

1° $d(\mathrm{id}, \mathcal{O}, b) = \begin{cases} 1 & \text{if } b \in \mathcal{O}, \\ 0 & \text{if } b \notin \overline{\mathcal{O}}. \end{cases}$

2° $d(\varphi, \mathcal{O}, b) \neq 0$ implies there is an $x \in \mathcal{O}$ such that $\varphi(x) = b$.

3° $d(\varphi, \mathcal{O}, b) = 0$ if $b \notin \varphi(\mathcal{O})$.

4° (*Additivity-excision property*): If $\mathcal{O}_1, \mathcal{O}_2 \subset \mathcal{O}$ are open with $\mathcal{O}_1 \cap \mathcal{O}_2 = \varnothing$ and $b \notin \varphi(\overline{\mathcal{O}} \setminus (\mathcal{O}_1 \cup \mathcal{O}_2))$, then $d(\varphi, \mathcal{O}, b) = d(\varphi, \mathcal{O}_1, b) + d(\varphi, \mathcal{O}_2, b)$.

5° (*Continuity in* φ): $d(\varphi, \mathcal{O}, b) = d(\psi, \mathcal{O}, b)$ for all ψ near φ.

Property 5° follows from a straightforward application of the Inverse Function Theorem. In 5°, ψ near φ refers to the C^1 norm.

The notion of degree given above and properties 1°–5° extend to all $\varphi \in C(\overline{\mathcal{O}}, \mathbf{R}^n)$ and $b \in \mathbf{R}^n \setminus \varphi(\partial\mathcal{O})$ with "near" in 5° now referring to the $C(\overline{\mathcal{O}}, \mathbf{R}^n)$

topology. Of course the formula (4.2) is lost in making this extension. A useful and important consequence of 5° is

PROPOSITION 4.4. *If* $H \in C([0,1] \times \overline{\mathcal{O}}, \mathbf{R}^n)$ *and* $b \notin H([0,1] \times \partial\mathcal{O})$, *then* $d(H(t,\cdot),\mathcal{O},b) \equiv$ *constant for* $t \in [0,1]$.

PROOF. Our above remarks imply that $d(H(t,\cdot),\mathcal{O},b)$ is defined for all $t \in [0,1]$. By 5° and the definition of degree, the mapping $t \to d(H(t,\cdot),\mathcal{O},b)$ is continuous and integer valued. Since $[0,1]$ is connected, the mapping must be constant.

COROLLARY 4.5. *If* $\varphi, \psi \in C(\overline{\mathcal{O}}, \mathbf{R}^n)$, $\varphi = \psi$ *on* $\partial\mathcal{O}$, *and* $b \in \mathbf{R}^n \setminus \varphi(\partial\mathcal{O})$, *then* $d(\varphi,\mathcal{O},b) = d(\psi,\mathcal{O},b)$.

PROOF. Set $H(t,x) = t\varphi(x) + (1-t)\psi(x)$ and invoke Proposition 4.4.

The definition of degree given above and its properties extend to an infinite dimensional setting as follows: E is a real Banach space, $\mathcal{O} \subset E$ is a bounded and open set, $\Phi \in C(\overline{\mathcal{O}}, E)$ with $\Phi(u) = u - T(u)$ and T compact, and $b \in E \setminus \Phi(\partial\mathcal{O})$. The resulting degree—still denoted by $d(\Phi,\mathcal{O},b)$—is called the *Leray-Schauder degree* (see [**LJS** or **S2**]).

With these preliminaries in hand, we turn to the Saddle Point Theorem [**R4**]:

THEOREM 4.6. *Let* $E = V \oplus X$, *where* E *is a real Banach space and* $V \neq \{0\}$ *and is finite dimensional. Suppose* $I \in C^1(E,\mathbf{R})$, *satisfies (PS), and*

(I_3) *there is a constant* α *and a bounded neighborhood* D *of* 0 *in* V *such that* $I|_{\partial D} \le \alpha$, *and*

(I_4) *there is a constant* $\beta > \alpha$ *such that* $I|_X \ge \beta$.

Then I *possesses a critical value* $c \ge \beta$. *Moreover* c *can be characterized as*

$$c = \inf_{h\in\Gamma} \max_{u\in\overline{D}} I(h(u)), \tag{4.7}$$

where

$$\Gamma = \{h \in C(\overline{D}, E) | h = \text{id } on\ \partial D\}.$$

PROOF. Let P denote the projector of E onto V obtained from the given splitting of E. If $h \in \Gamma$, $Ph \in C(D,V)$. Moreover $u \in \partial D$ implies $Ph(u) = Pu = u \neq 0$. Identifying V with $\mathbf{R}^n$ for some n, $d(Ph,D,0)$ is defined and by Corollary 4.5 and 1° of (4.3),

$$d(Ph,D,0) = d(\text{id},D,0) = 1.$$

Hence by 2° of (4.3), there exists an $x \in D$ such that $Ph(x) = 0$. Consequently for each $h \in \Gamma$, there is an $x = x(h) \in D$ such that

$$h(x) = (\text{id} - P)h(x) \in X. \tag{4.8}$$

Hypothesis (I_4) now implies

$$\max_{u\in\overline{D}} I(h(u)) \ge I(h(x)) \ge \beta.$$

Thus by (4.7), $c \geq \beta$. To show that c is a critical value of I requires a familiar argument. If $K_c = \emptyset$, we set $\bar{\varepsilon} = \frac{1}{2}(\beta - \alpha)$ and invoke Theorem A4 obtaining ε and η as usual. Choose $h \in \Gamma$ such that

$$\max_{u \in \overline{D}} I(h(u)) \leq c + \varepsilon. \tag{4.9}$$

If $\eta(1, h) \in \Gamma$, by (4.9) and 7° of Theorem A.4, we get our usual contradiction. Since $\eta(1, h) \in C(\overline{D}, E)$, it belongs to Γ if $\eta(1, h(u)) = u$ for $u \in \partial D$. But for such u, $h(u) = u$ and $\eta(1, u) = u$. This last equality follows via 2° of Theorem A.4 since $I(u) \leq \alpha < \alpha + \bar{\varepsilon} \leq \beta - \bar{\varepsilon} \leq c + \varepsilon$ via our choice of $\bar{\varepsilon}$. The proof is complete.

REMARKS 4.10. (i) If $V = \{0\}$, (I_3) makes no sense but (I_4) and Theorem 2.7 imply I has a critical value.

(ii) Hypotheses (I_3)–(I_4) will be satisfied if e.g. I is concave on V, convex on X, and appropriately coercive as one approaches infinity along these subspaces.

Theorem 4.6 was motivated by a PDE existence result due to Ahmad, Lazer, and Paul [**ALP**] (see also [**Am, AZ**]). As an application of Theorem 4.6 a version of a result in [**ALP**] will be given next. Consider

$$\begin{aligned} -\Delta u &= \lambda a(x) u + p(x, u), \qquad x \in \Omega, \\ u &= 0, \qquad x \in \partial\Omega, \end{aligned} \tag{4.11}$$

where p satisfies (p_1) and (p_2) with $s = 0$. If λ is not an eigenvalue of (2.39), then (p_2) with $s = 0$ and standard elliptic estimates imply an a priori bound for solutions of (4.11) in $W_0^{2,\beta}(\Omega)$ for e.g. $\beta > n$. Then one can use the linear elliptic theory for such spaces and the Schauder Fixed Point Theorem to get a solution of (4.11). Thus an interesting question to study is what happens when λ is an eigenvalue of (2.40).

THEOREM 4.12. *Suppose* $\lambda = \lambda_k < \lambda_{k+1}$ *and* p *satisfies* $(p_1), (p_2)$ *with* $s = 0$, *and*

(p_7) $P(x, \xi) = \int_0^\xi p(x, t)\, dt \to \infty$ *as* $|\xi| \to \infty$ *uniformly for* $x \in \Omega$.

Then (4.11) *possesses a weak solution.*

PROOF. Let

$$I(u) = \int_\Omega \left(\frac{1}{2} |\nabla u|^2 - \frac{\lambda}{2} a u^2 - P(x, u) \right) dx$$

for $u \in E \equiv W_0^{1,2}(\Omega)$. Since (p_1) and (p_2) hold, $I \in C^1(E, \mathbf{R})$. Let $V \equiv \operatorname{span}\{v_1, \ldots, v_k\}$, where v_j is an eigenfunction of (2.39) corresponding to λ_j and normalized so that

$$\int_\Omega |\nabla v_j|^2\, dx = 1 = \lambda_j \int_\Omega a v_j^2\, dv.$$

Let $X = \overline{\operatorname{span}\{v_j | j \geq k+1\}}$ so $X = V^\perp$. Therefore $E = V \oplus X$. We will show that I satisfies (I_3), (I_4), and (PS). Then Theorem 4.12 follows from Theorem 4.6.

If $u \in X$, then $u = \sum_{j=k+1}^{\infty} a_j v_j$ and

$$(4.13)\qquad \int_\Omega (|\nabla u|^2 - \lambda_k a u^2)\, dx = \sum_{j=k+1}^{\infty} a_j^2 \left(1 - \frac{\lambda_k}{\lambda_j}\right) \geq \left(1 - \frac{\lambda_k}{\lambda_{k+1}}\right) \|u\|^2.$$

Let $M \equiv \sup_{x\in\overline{\Omega}, \xi\in\mathbf{R}} |p(x,\xi)|$. Then

$$(4.14)\qquad \left|\int_\Omega P(x,u)\, dx\right| \leq M \int_\Omega |u|\, dx \leq M_1 \|u\|$$

for all $u \in E$ via the Hölder and Poincaré inequalities. Combining (4.13)–(4.14) shows I is bounded from below on X, i.e. (I_4) holds. Next if $u \in V$, then $u = u^0 + u^-$, where $u^0 \in E^0 \equiv \operatorname{span}\{v_j | \lambda_j = \lambda_k\}$ and $u^- \in E^- \equiv \operatorname{span}\{v_j | \lambda_j < \lambda_k\}$. Then

(4.15)

$$I(u) = \frac{1}{2} \sum_{j<k} a_j^2 \left(1 - \frac{\lambda_k}{\lambda_j}\right) - \int_\Omega P(x,u^0)\, dx + \int_\Omega (P(x,u^0+u^-) - P(x,u^0))\, dx.$$

Estimating the last term as in (4.14),

$$(4.16)\qquad I(u) \leq -M_2 \|u^-\|^2 - \int_\Omega P(x,u^0)\, dx + M_1 \|u^-\|.$$

Now (4.16) and (p_7) show $I(u) \to -\infty$ as $u \to \infty$ in V. Hence I satisfies (I_3).

Lastly to verify (PS), by Proposition B.35 it suffices to show that $|I(u_m)| \leq K$ and $I'(u_m) \to 0$ implies (u_m) is bounded. Writing $u_m = u_m^0 + u_m^- + u_m^+$, where $u_m^0 \in E^0$, $u_m^- \in E^-$, $u_m^+ \in X$, for large m:

$(4.17)^{\pm}$

$$|I'(u_m)u_m^{\pm}| = \left|\int_\Omega [\nabla u_m \cdot \nabla u_m^{\pm} - \lambda_k a u_m u_m^{\pm} - p(x,u_m)u_m^{\pm}]\, dx\right| \leq \|u_m^{\pm}\|.$$

Consequently since $X = V^\perp$, by $(4.17)^+$, (4.13), (P_2), and an estimate like (4.14),

$$(4.18)\qquad \|u_m^+\| \geq \left(1 - \frac{\lambda_k}{\lambda_{k+1}}\right) \|u_m^+\|^2 - M_1 \|u_m^+\|$$

which shows that $\{\|u_m^+\|\}$ is bounded. Similarly $(4.17)^-$ shows $\{\|u_m^-\|\}$ is bounded. Finally we claim that $\{\|u_m^0\|\}$ is also bounded. Then (u_m) is bounded in E and we are through.

To verify the claim, observe that

(4.19)

$$\begin{aligned} K \geq |I(u_m)| = \Bigg|\int_\Omega \{\tfrac{1}{2}[|\nabla u_m^+|^2 + |\nabla u_m^-|^2 \\ - \lambda_k a((u_m^+)^2 + (u_m^-)^2)] - (P(x,u_m) - P(x,u_m^0))\}\, dx \\ - \int_\Omega P(x,u_m^0)\, dx\Bigg|. \end{aligned}$$

By what has already been shown, the first term on the right is bounded independently of m. Therefore

$$K \geq \left| \int_\Omega P(x, u_m^0)\, dx \right| - K_1, \tag{4.20}$$

so $(\int_\Omega P(x, u_m^0)\, dx)$ is bounded. This implies (u_m^0) is bounded. Indeed

LEMMA 4.21. *If P satisfies $(p_1), (p_2)$, and (p_7), then*

$$\int_\Omega P(x, v)\, dx \to \infty \tag{4.22}$$

as $v \to \infty$ uniformly for $v \in E^0$.

PROOF. By (p_1)–(p_2), the functional in (4.22) belongs to $C^1(E, \mathbf{R})$. By (p_7) for any $k > 0$, there is a d_k such that $P(x, \xi) \geq k$ if $|\xi| \geq d_k$ for all $x \in \overline{\Omega}$. Let $v \in E^0$ and write $v = t\varphi$ where $\varphi \in \partial B_1$. Then

$$\int_\Omega P(x, t\varphi)\, dx \geq \int_{\Omega_k} P(x, t\varphi)\, dx - M_0, \tag{4.23}$$

where Ω_k $(= \Omega_k(t\varphi)) = \{x \in \Omega | P(x, t\varphi(x)) \geq k\}$ and

$$M_0 \geq (\operatorname{meas} \Omega) \left| \inf_{x \in \overline{\Omega}, \xi \in \mathbf{R}} P(x, \xi) \right| .$$

Since $\varphi \not\equiv 0$, there is an $x_0 = x_0(\varphi) \in \Omega$ and $\;\; > 0$ such that $\varphi \neq 0$ in $B_{2r}(x_0)$ (the ball of radius $2r$ about x_0). Therefore by (p_7), for all large t, $\Omega_k \supset B_r(x_0)$ and $P(x, t\varphi) \to \infty$ on $B_r(x_0)$ as $t \to \infty$. Hence the right-hand side of (4.23) $\to \infty$ as $t \to \infty$. Since $\partial B_1 \cap E^0$ is compact, (4.22) holds uniformly for $v \in E^0$ and the lemma is proved.

REMARK 4.24. If (p_7) is replaced by $P(x, \xi) \to -\infty$ as $|\xi| \to \infty$, the above arguments can easily be modified to handle this case.

5. Some Generalizations of the Mountain Pass Theorem

This section begins with a generalization of the Mountain Pass Theorem in which (I_1) is weakened. This enables us to treat (2.9) where the nonlinearity also contains a linear part at 0. Then an abstract critical point theorem is proved which contains earlier results both of mountain pass and saddle point type. To describe and state it, we will introduce an infinite dimensional notion of linking.

To motivate the first abstract result of this section, consider

$$\begin{aligned} -\Delta u &= \lambda a(x)u + p(x,u), \qquad x \in \Omega, \\ u &= 0, \qquad x \in \partial\Omega, \end{aligned} \tag{5.1}$$

where p satisfies (p_1)–(p_4). This differs from the case treated in Theorem 2.15 due to the presence of the linear term in (5.1). The corresponding functional on E is

$$I(u) = \int_\Omega \left[\frac{1}{2}|\nabla u|^2 - \frac{\lambda}{2}au^2 - P(x,u)\right] dx. \tag{5.2}$$

If $\lambda < \lambda_1$, with λ_1 as in (2.39), then $(\int_\Omega(|\nabla u|^2 - \lambda a u^2)\,dx)^{1/2}$ can be taken as a norm on E, I satisfies (I_1), and one can use the Mountain Pass Theorem to establish the existence of a weak solution to (5.1) (and even a positive solution). However if $\lambda > \lambda_1$, (I_1) no longer holds so our previous existence mechanism fails. The next result from [**R5**] gives us a tool to treat problems where a milder version of (I_1) is satisfied.

THEOREM 5.3. *Let E be a real Banach space with $E = V \oplus X$, where V is finite dimensional. Suppose $I \in C^1(E, \mathbf{R})$, satisfies (PS), and*

(I_1') there are constants $\rho, \alpha > 0$ such that $I|_{\partial B_\rho \cap X} \geq \alpha$, and

(I_5) there is an $e \in \partial B_1 \cap X$ and $R > \rho$ such that if $Q \equiv (\overline{B}_R \cap V) \oplus \{re | 0 < r < R\}$, then $I|_{\partial Q} \leq 0$.

Then I possesses a critical value $c \geq \alpha$ which can be characterized as

$$c \equiv \inf_{h\in\Gamma} \max_{u\in Q} I(h(u)), \tag{5.4}$$

where

$$\Gamma = \{h \in C(\overline{Q}, E) | h = \text{id } on\ \partial Q\}.$$

REMARKS 5.5. (i) ∂Q refers to the boundary of Q relative to $V \oplus \text{span}\{e\}$.

(ii) If $V = \{0\}$, then $X = E$ and (I_1') reduces to (I_1). If further $I(0) = 0$, (I_5) becomes (I_2). Thus Theorem 5.3 is a generalization of the Mountain Pass Theorem.

(iii) Suppose $I|_V \leq 0$ and there is an $e \in \partial B_1 \cap X$ and an $\overline{R} > \rho$ such that $I(u) \leq 0$ for $u \in V \oplus \text{span}\{e\}$ and $\|u\| \geq \overline{R}$. Then for any large R, Q as defined in (I_5) satisfies $I|_Q \leq 0$.

PROOF OF THEOREM 5.3. The only novelty in the proof is to show that

$$c \geq \alpha. \tag{5.6}$$

Once that has been done, a familiar argument shows that c is a critical value of I. Indeed if not, set $\overline{\varepsilon} = \alpha/2$ and invoke Theorem A.4 to get $\varepsilon \in (0, \overline{\varepsilon})$ and $\eta \in C([0,1] \times E, E)$ such that

$$\eta(1, A_{c+\varepsilon}) \subset A_{c-\varepsilon}. \tag{5.7}$$

Choose $h \in \Gamma$ such that

$$\max_{u \in Q} I(h(u)) \leq c + \varepsilon. \tag{5.8}$$

Then since $I(u) \leq 0$ on ∂Q, 2° of Theorem A.4 and our choice of $\overline{\varepsilon}$ imply that $\eta(1, h(u)) = u$ for $u \in \partial Q$. Hence $\eta(1, h(u)) \in \Gamma$. But (5.8) and (5.4) then imply

$$c \leq \max_{u \in Q} I(\eta(1, h(u))) \leq c - \varepsilon,$$

a contradiction.

To verify (5.6), it suffices to establish the following *intersection theorem*:

PROPOSITION 5.9. *If $h \in \Gamma$, then*

$$h(Q) \cap \partial B_\rho \cap X \neq \emptyset. \tag{5.10}$$

Given Proposition 5.9, let $h \in \Gamma$ and $w \in h(Q) \cap \partial B_\rho \cap X$. Then

$$\max_{u \in Q} I(h(u)) \geq I(w) \geq \inf_{v \in \partial B_\rho \cap X} I(v) \geq \alpha, \tag{5.11}$$

the last inequality following via (I_1'). Since h was arbitrary, (5.4) and (5.11) imply (5.6).

PROOF OF PROPOSITION 5.9. Let P denote the projector of E onto V for the given splitting. Then (5.10) is equivalent to

$$\begin{cases} Ph(u) = 0, \\ \|(\text{id} - P)h(u)\| = \rho \end{cases} \tag{5.12}$$

for some $u \in Q$ (depending on h). Expressing $u \in \overline{Q}$ as $u = v + re$, where $v \in \overline{B}_R \cap V$ and $0 \leq r \leq R$, define

$$\Phi(r, v) = (\|(\text{id} - P)h(v + re)\|, Ph(v + re)).$$

Then $\Phi \in C(\mathbf{R} \times V, \mathbf{R} \times V)$. Since $h|_{\partial Q} = \text{id}$, if $u \in \partial Q$,

$$\Phi(r, v) = (\|re\|, v) = (r, v), \tag{5.13}$$

i.e. $\Phi = \text{id}$ on ∂Q. In particular $\Phi(r,v) \neq (\rho,0)$ for $u \in \partial Q$ since by (I_5), $(\rho,0) \in Q$. Identifying $\mathbf{R} \times V$ with $\mathbf{R}^n$ for some n, we see that $d(\Phi, Q, (\rho,0))$ is defined and by (5.13), Corollary 4.5, and 1° of (4.3),

$$d(\Phi, Q, (\rho,0)) = d(\text{id}, Q, (\rho,0)) = 1. \tag{5.14}$$

Hence by 2° of (4.3), there exists $u \in Q$ such that $\Phi(u) = (\rho,0)$, i.e. (5.12) is satisfied and the proposition is proved.

REMARK 5.15. The above proof shows Γ could have been chosen in other ways, e.g.

$$\{h \in C(\overline{Q}, E) | d(h, Q, (\rho,0)) \neq 0\}.$$

We now turn to an application of Theorem 5.3 to (5.1).

THEOREM 5.16. *Suppose p satisfies (p_1)–(p_4) and*
(p_8) $\xi p(x,\xi) \geq 0$ *for all* $\xi \in \mathbf{R}$.
Then for all $\lambda \in \mathbf{R}$, (5.1) *possesses a nontrivial weak solution.*

PROOF. If $\lambda < \lambda_1$, the smallest eigenvalue of (2.40), the result follows from remarks made at the beginning of this chapter. Thus suppose $\lambda \geq \lambda_1$, e.g. $\lambda \in [\lambda_k, \lambda_{k+1}]$. We will show I as defined by (5.2) satisfies the hypotheses of Theorem 5.3. Clearly $I \in C^1(E, \mathbf{R})$ via (p_1)–(p_2). Set $V \equiv \text{span}\{v_1, \dots, v_k\}$ and $X = V^\perp$, where the v_j's are as following (2.40). For $u \in X$,

$$\int_\Omega (|\nabla u|^2 - \lambda u^2)\, dx \geq \left(1 - \frac{\lambda}{\lambda_{k+1}}\right) \|u\|^2$$

as in (4.13) while by (p_3) (and the proof of Theorem 2.15),

$$\int_\Omega P(x,u)\, dx = o(\|u\|^2) \quad \text{as } u \to 0.$$

Hence I satisfies (I_1'). To verify (I_5), by Remark 5.5(iii), it suffices to show (a) $I|_V \leq 0$ and (b) there is an $e \in \partial B_1 \cap X$ and $\overline{R} > \rho$ such that $I(u) \leq 0$ for $u \in V \oplus \text{span}\{e\} \equiv \tilde{E}$ and $\|u\| > \overline{R}$. But (a) follows from (p_8) and (b) with e.g. $e = v_{k+1}$ on noting that the argument of (2.16)–(2.17) is uniform for finite dimensional subspaces of E.

It only remains to check that I satisfies (PS) or (via Proposition B.35) that $|I(u_m)| \leq M$ and $I'(u_m) \to 0$ implies (u_m) is bounded. Choose $\beta \in (\mu^{-1}, 2^{-1})$. Then for m large and $u = u_m$

$$\begin{aligned} M + \beta\|u\| &\geq I(u) - \beta I'(u)u \\ &= \int_\Omega [(\tfrac{1}{2} - \beta)|\nabla u|^2 - \lambda(\tfrac{1}{2} - \beta)au^2 + \beta p(x,u)u - P(x,u)]\, dx \\ &\geq (\tfrac{1}{2} - \beta)\|u\|^2 - \lambda(\tfrac{1}{2} - \beta)\|a\|_{L^\infty(\Omega)}\|u\|^2_{L^2(\Omega)} \\ &\quad + (\beta\mu - 1)\int_\Omega P(x,u)\, dx - a_5 \\ &\geq (\tfrac{1}{2} - \beta)\|u\|^2 - \lambda(\tfrac{1}{2} - \beta)\|a\|_{L^\infty(\Omega)}\|u\|^2_{L^2(\Omega)} \\ &\quad + (\beta\mu - 1)a_6\|u\|^\mu_{L^\mu(\Omega)} - a_7, \end{aligned} \tag{5.17}$$

where (p_4) and (2.14) have been used. By standard inequalities, since $\mu > 2$, for $\varepsilon > 0$,

(5.18) $$\|u\|_{L^2(\Omega)} \leq a_8 \|u\|_{L^\mu(\Omega)} \leq a_9 K(\varepsilon) + \varepsilon \|u\|^\mu_{L^\mu(\Omega)},$$

where $K(\varepsilon) \to \infty$ as $\varepsilon \to 0$. Choosing ε so small that the L^μ term in (5.17) absorbs (with the aid of (5.18)) the L^2 term, we see (u_m) is bounded in E and the proof is complete.

REMARK 5.19. In Corollary 2.23, we show that (2.9) possesses a positive solution. The same arguments apply to the current setting if $\lambda < \lambda_1$. However if $\lambda \geq \lambda_1$, we cannot expect a positive solution of (5.1). Indeed if v_1 is an eigenfunction corresponding to λ_1 in (2.40), we can assume $v_1 > 0$ in Ω. Therefore if u is a solution of (5.1),

(5.20) $$\begin{aligned}\int_\Omega (\lambda a u + p(x,u)) v_1 \, dx &= \int_\Omega (-\Delta u) v_1 \, dx \\ &= \int_\Omega (-\Delta v_1) u \, dx = \lambda_1 \int_\Omega a v_1 u \, dx.\end{aligned}$$

Consequently

(5.21) $$(\lambda_1 - \lambda) \int_\Omega a u v_1 \, dx = \int_\Omega p(x,u) v_1 \, dx.$$

If u is positive in Ω, the left-hand side of (5.21) is nonpositive while by (p_8), the right-hand side is nonnegative. Thus there can only be a positive solution $u(x)$ if $\lambda = \lambda_1$ and $p(x, u(x)) \equiv 0$.

An examination of our abstract critical point theorems shows that an important ingredient in their proofs is an "intersection theorem" which allows us to show that the minimax values defined in these results are indeed critical values. E.g. in Theorem 5.3, this is carried out in Proposition 5.9 while in Theorem 4.6 it is done in (4.8). Our next goal is to introduce a topological notion of linking which modulo assumptions on the form of the functional will enable us to prove a result which contains both Theorems 4.6 and 5.3. It also enables us to weaken the splitting assumptions of these theorems.

Thus let E be a real Banach space with $E = E_1 \oplus E_2$, where both E_1 and E_2 may be infinite dimensional. Let P_1, P_2 be the projectors of E onto E_1, E_2 associated with the given splitting of E. Set

$$\begin{aligned}\mathcal{S} \equiv \{\Phi \in C([0,1] \times E, E) | \Phi(0,u) = u \text{ and } P_2\Phi(t,u) = \\ P_2 u - K(t,u), \text{ where } K\colon [0,1] \times E \to E_2 \text{ is compact}\}.\end{aligned}$$

Recall K compact means it is continuous and maps bounded sets to relatively compact sets. Let $S, Q \subset E$ with $Q \subset \tilde{E}$, a given subspace of E. Then ∂Q will refer to the boundary of Q in that subspace. We say S and ∂Q *link* if whenever $\Phi \in \mathcal{S}$ and $\Phi(t, \partial Q) \cap S = \emptyset$ for all $t \in [0,1]$, then $\Phi(t, Q) \cap S \neq \emptyset$ for all $t \in [0,1]$. This notion and the examples below are due to Benci and the author [**BR**]. For heuristic purposes, one can think of the sets S and ∂Q as linking if every manifold modelled on Q and sharing the same boundary intersects S. We will give two examples of such linking corresponding to what occurs in Theorems 4.6 and 5.3.

EXAMPLE 5.22. Let $Q \equiv B \cap E_2$, where B is a neighborhood of 0 in E_2, $\tilde{E} \equiv E_2$, $q \in Q$, and $S \equiv q + E_1$. Suppose $\Phi \in \mathcal{S}$ and

$$\Phi(t, \partial Q) \cap (q + E_1) = \varnothing \quad \text{for all } t \in [0,1]. \tag{5.23}$$

We claim $\Phi(t, Q) \cap S \neq \varnothing$ for all $t \in [0,1]$, i.e. there is a $w = w(t) \in Q$ such that $P_2\Phi(t, w(t)) = q$. For $u \in E_2$, set $\Psi(t,u) \equiv P_2\Phi(t,u) = u - K(t,u)$. By (5.23), $\Psi(t,u) \neq q$ for $u \in \partial Q$. Therefore $d(\Psi(t,\cdot), Q, q)$ is defined for $t \in [0,1]$ and by the infinite dimensional versions of Propositions 4.4 and 4.3, for any $t \in [0,1]$,

$$d(\Psi(t,\cdot), Q, q) = d(\Psi(0,\cdot), Q, q) = d(\mathrm{id}, Q, q) = 1. \tag{5.24}$$

Hence there is a $w(t) \in Q$ as desired and S and ∂Q link.

REMARK 5.25. Setting $q = 0$, $S = X$, and $Q = D$, we are in the setting of the Saddle Point Theorem.

EXAMPLE 5.26. Let $\rho > 0$, $S \equiv \partial B_\rho \cap E_1$, $e \in E_1 \cap \partial B_1$, $r_1 > \rho$, $r_2 > 0$, $Q \equiv \{re | r \in [0, r_1]\} \oplus (B_{r_2} \cap E_2)$, and $\tilde{E} \equiv \mathrm{span}\{e\} \oplus E_2$. Suppose $\Phi \in S$ and

$$\Phi(t, \partial Q) \cap S = \varnothing \quad \text{for all } t \in [0,1]. \tag{5.27}$$

We claim for each $t \in [0,1]$, there is a $w(t) \in Q$ such that $\Phi(t, w(t)) \in S$, i.e. $P_2\Phi(t, w(t)) = 0$ and $\|P_1\Phi(t, w(t))\| = \rho$. For $u \in E_2$ and $r \in \mathbf{R}$, set

$$\Psi(t, (r,u)) \equiv (\|P_1\Phi(t, re+u)\|, P_2\Phi(t, re+u)).$$

By (5.27), $d(\Psi(t,\cdot), Q, (\rho, 0))$ is well defined and as in (5.24),

$$d(\Psi(t,(r,u)), Q, (\rho, 0)) = 1.$$

Consequently there is a $w(t)$ as claimed and S and ∂Q link.

REMARK 5.28. Setting $E_1 = X$, $E_2 = V$, and $r_1 = R = r_2$, the relationship between Example 5.26 and Theorem 5.3 becomes clear.

Now we are ready to state a critical point theorem which unifies Theorems 4.6 and 5.3.

THEOREM 5.29. *Let E be a real Hilbert space with $E = E_1 \oplus E_2$ and $E_2 = E_1^\perp$. Suppose $I \in C^1(E, \mathbf{R})$, satisfies (PS), and*

(I_5) *$I(u) = \frac{1}{2}(Lu, u) + b(u)$, where $Lu = L_1P_1u + L_2P_2u$ and $L_i \colon E_i \to E_i$ is bounded and selfadjoint, $i = 1, 2$,*

(I_6) *b' is compact, and*

(I_7) *there exists a subspace $\tilde{E} \subset E$ and sets $S \subset E$, $Q \subset \tilde{E}$ and constants $\alpha > \omega$ such that*

(i) *$S \subset E_1$ and $I|_S \geq \alpha$,*

(ii) *Q is bounded and $I|_{\partial Q} \leq \omega$,*

(iii) *S and ∂Q link.*

Then I possesses a critical value $c \geq \alpha$.

REMARK 5.30. Roughly speaking, c will be obtained as the minimax of I over all surfaces modelled on Q. Although the hypotheses of Theorem 5.29 are more restrictive than in our earlier results because of (I_5), (I_6), $E_2 = E_1^{\perp}$, etc., it is easy to check that the PDE applications presented earlier do indeed satisfy these conditions.

PROOF OF THEOREM 5.29. The proof follows the same lines as our earlier results. An appropriate class of sets will be introduced and c defined as the minimax of I over this class. Let

$$\Gamma \equiv \{h \in C([0,1] \times E, E) | h \text{ satisfies } (\Gamma_1)\text{-}(\Gamma_3)\},$$

where

(Γ_1) $h(0,u) = u$,

(Γ_2) $h(t,u) = u$ for $u \in \partial Q$, and

(Γ_3) $h(t,u) = e^{\theta(t,u)L}u + K(t,u)$, where $\theta \in C([0,1] \times E, \mathbf{R})$ and K is compact.

Note that id $\in \Gamma$ and if $g, h \in \Gamma$ so is $g \circ h$ with

$$\theta_{g \circ h} = \theta_g(t, h(t,u)) + \theta_h(t,u)$$

and

$$K_{g \circ h}(t,u) = e^{\theta_g(t,h(t,u))L} K_h(t,u) + K_g(t, h(t,u)).$$

Also by (Γ_3) and (I_5),

$$h(t,u) = e^{\theta L_1}u_1 + e^{\theta L_2}u_2 + K(t,u), \tag{5.31}$$

where $u_i = P_i u$, $i = 1, 2$. The mappings in Γ have an important intersection property.

PROPOSITION 5.32. *If $h \in \Gamma$, then*

$$h(t,Q) \cap S \neq \varnothing \quad \textit{for each } t \in [0,1]. \tag{5.33}$$

PROOF. Equation (5.33) is equivalent to solving

$$P_1 h(t,u) \in S, \qquad P_2 h(t,u) = 0 \tag{5.34}$$

and via (5.31) the latter equation is equivalent to

$$u_2 + e^{-\theta L_2} K_2(t,u) = 0, \tag{5.35}$$

where $K_2 = P_2 K$. Define

$$\Phi(t,u) \equiv P_1 h(t,u) + u_2 + e^{-\theta L_2} K_2(t,u)$$

so by (5.34)–(5.35), (5.33) is equivalent to

$$\Phi(t,Q) \cap S \neq \varnothing \quad \text{for each } t \in [0,1]. \tag{5.36}$$

By its definition, $\Phi \in \mathcal{S}$. Thus to prove (5.36), by (I_7)(iii), it suffices to show that

$$\Phi(t, \partial Q) \cap S = \varnothing \quad \text{for each } t \in [0,1]. \tag{5.37}$$

But $\Phi(t,u) = u$ if $u \in \partial Q$ by (Γ_2) and $\partial Q \cap S = \emptyset$ by (i) and (ii) of (I_7). Hence (5.37) holds and the proposition is proved.

Now we can define

$$c = \inf_{h \in \Gamma} \sup_{u \in Q} I(h(1,u)). \tag{5.38}$$

By hypothesis (I_6), b is weakly continuous (i.e. if (u_m) converges weakly to u, $b(u_m) \to b(u)$) [**K**]. The boundedness of Q and (I_5) then imply $\sup_{u \in Q} I(u) < \infty$. Since id $\in \Gamma$, it follows that $c < \infty$. By Proposition 5.32 and (i) of (I_7),

$$c \geq \alpha. \tag{5.39}$$

To complete the proof, we must show that c is a critical value of I. Let $\bar{\varepsilon} = \frac{1}{2}(\alpha - \omega)$. By our usual argument, if c is not a critical value of I, there is an $\varepsilon \in (0, \bar{\varepsilon})$ and $\eta \in C([0,1] \times E, E)$ given by Theorem A.4 such that $\eta(1, A_{c+\varepsilon}) \subset A_{c-\varepsilon}$. Choose $h \in \Gamma$ such that

$$\sup_{u \in Q} I(h(1,u)) \leq c + \varepsilon.$$

Then our usual argument leads to a contradiction provided that $\eta \circ h \in \Gamma$. By an above remark, this will be the case if $\eta \in \Gamma$. By 1° of Theorem A.4, η satisfies (Γ_1) and by 2° of that theorem, (5.39), (I_7)(ii), and the choice of $\bar{\varepsilon}$, (Γ_2) holds. Finally by Proposition A.18, η also satisfies (Γ_3).

REMARK 5.40. See [**Ni**, **BR**, and **Ho1**] for other such results.

An application of Theorem 5.29 will be given in the next chapter.

6. Applications to Hamiltonian Systems

This chapter contains applications of Theorem 5.29 to problems in which both E_1 and E_2 are infinite dimensional. Such situations arise in studying the existence of periodic solutions of Hamiltonian systems. For $p, q \in \mathbf{R}^n$ and $H \in C^1(\mathbf{R}^{2n}, \mathbf{R})$, the system of ordinary differential equations

$$\begin{cases} \dot{p} = -H_q(p,q) \\ \dot{q} = H_p(p,q) \end{cases} \tag{6.1}$$

is called a Hamiltonian system. Setting $z = (p,q)$ and $\mathcal{J} = \left(\begin{smallmatrix} 0 & -I \\ I & 0 \end{smallmatrix}\right)$, where I is the n-dimensional identity matrix, (6.1) can be written more concisely as

$$\dot{z} = \mathcal{J} H_z(z). \tag{6.2}$$

One of the basic properties of such systems is that if $z(t)$ is a solution, $H(z(t)) \equiv$ const, i.e. "energy" is conserved. Indeed

$$\frac{d}{dt} H(z(t)) = H_z \cdot \dot{z} = H_z \cdot \mathcal{J} H_z \equiv 0 \tag{6.3}$$

via (6.1) or (6.2).

It will be shown that (6.2) possesses periodic solutions under certain conditions on H. Before giving a variational formulation of (6.2), some preliminary material on function spaces and norms is needed.

Let $L^2(S^1, \mathbf{R}^m)$ denote the set of m-tuples of 2π periodic functions which are square integrable. If $z \in L^2(S^1, \mathbf{R}^m)$, it has a Fourier expansion $z = \sum_{j \in \mathbf{Z}} a_j e^{ijt}$, where $a_j \in C^m$, $a_{-j} = \bar{a}_j$, and $\sum_{j \in \mathbf{Z}} |a_j|^2 < \infty$. Set

$$\|z\|_{W^{\theta,2}} \equiv \left(\sum_{j \in \mathbf{Z}} (1 + |j|^{2\theta}) |a_j|^2 \right)^{1/2}$$

and let

$$W^{\theta,2}(S^1, \mathbf{R}^m) \equiv \{ z \in L^2(S^1, \mathbf{R}^m) \mid \|z\|_{W^{\theta,2}} < \infty \}.$$

We will mainly be interested in $\theta = \frac{1}{2}$, $m = 2n$, and $E \equiv W^{1/2,2}(S^1, \mathbf{R}^{2n})$. For e.g. smooth $z = (p,q) \in E$ where p and q are each n-tuples, set

$$A(z) \equiv \int_0^{2\pi} p \cdot \dot{q} \, dt. \tag{6.4}$$

Then it is easy to check that

$$|A(z)| \le \text{const} \left(\sum_{j \in \mathbf{Z}} |j|\, |p_j|^2 \right)^{1/2} \left(\sum_{j \in \mathbf{Z}} |j|\, |q_j|^2 \right)^{1/2} \le \text{const}\, \|z\|_E^2.$$

Therefore A extends to all of E as a continuous quadratic form. This extension will still be denoted by A.

Let $e_1, \ldots, e_{2n}$ denote the usual bases in $\mathbf{R}^{2n}$ and set

$$E^0 \equiv \operatorname{span}\{e_1, \ldots, e_{2n}\},$$
$$E^+ \equiv \operatorname{span}\{(\sin jt)e_k - (\cos jt)e_{k+n}, (\cos jt)e_k + (\sin jt)e_{k+n} \mid j \in \mathbf{N}, 1 \le k \le n\},$$

and

$$E^- \equiv \operatorname{span}\{(\sin jt)e_k + (\cos jt)e_{k+n}, (\cos jt)e_k - (\sin jt)e_{k+n} \mid j \in \mathbf{N}, 1 \le k \le n\}.$$

Then $E = E^0 \oplus E^+ \oplus E^-$. In fact it is not difficult to verify that E^+, E^-, E^0 are respectively the subspaces of E on which A is positive definite, negative definite, and null, and these spaces are orthogonal with respect to the bilinear form

$$B[z, \varsigma] \equiv \int_0^{2\pi} (p \cdot \dot{\psi} + \varphi \cdot \dot{q})\, dt$$

associated with A. Here $z = (p, q)$ and $\varsigma = (\varphi, \psi)$. E.g. if $z \in E^+$ and $\varsigma \in E^-$, $B[z, \varsigma] = 0$ and $A(z + \varsigma) = A(z) + A(\varsigma)$. It is also easy to check that E^0, E^+, and E^- are mutually orthogonal in $L^2(S^1, \mathbf{R}^{2n})$.

These remarks show that if $z = z^0 + z^+ + z^- \in E$,

$$\|z\|^2 \equiv |z^0|^2 + A(z^+) - A(z^-) \tag{6.5}$$

serves as an equivalent norm on E. Henceforth we use the norm defined in (6.5) as the norm for E. The spaces E^0, E^+, E^- are mutually orthogonal with respect to the associated inner product via our above remarks.

One further analytical fact about E is needed.

PROPOSITION 6.6. *For each* $s \in [1, \infty)$, E *is compactly embedded in* $L^s(S^1, \mathbf{R}^{2n})$. *In particular there is an* $\alpha_s > 0$ *such that*

$$\|z\|_{L^s} \le \alpha_s \|z\| \tag{6.7}$$

for all $z \in E$.

PROOF. See [**Fr** or **R7**].

To obtain periodic solutions of (6.2), we are led to study critical points of an associated functional on E. Suppose $H \in C^1(\mathbf{R}^{2n}, \mathbf{R})$ and there is an $s \in (1, \infty)$ such that

$$|H(z)| \le a_1 + a_2 |z|^s \tag{6.8}$$

for all $z \in \mathbf{R}^{2n}$. Then by Proposition B.39,

$$\mathcal{H}(z) \equiv \int_0^{2\pi} H(z)\,dt \in C^1(E, \mathbf{R})$$

as is $I(z)$ defined by

$$I(z) = A(z) - \mathcal{H}(z). \tag{6.9}$$

If $z \in C^1(S^1, \mathbf{R}^{2n})$ is a critical point of I and $\varsigma = (\varphi, \psi) \in E$, a computation shows that

$$I'(z)\varsigma = 0 = \int_0^{2\pi} [(-\dot{p} - H_q(z)) \cdot \psi + (\dot{q} - H_p(z)) \cdot \varphi]\,dt$$

which implies that z satisfies (6.2). More generally a critical point z of I in E will be a weak solution of (6.2). However a simple regularity argument then shows $z \in C^1(S^1, \mathbf{R}^{2n})$ (see the proof of Theorem 6.10 below). Thus we are interested in critical points of (6.9).

THEOREM 6.10 [**R6**]. *Suppose $H \in C^1(\mathbf{R}^{2n}, \mathbf{R})$ and satisfies*

(H_1) $H \geq 0$,

(H_2) $H(z) = o(|z|^2)$ as $|z| \to 0$, and

(H_3) there are constants $\mu > 2$ and $\overline{r} > 0$ such that $0 < \mu H(z) \leq z \cdot H_z(z)$ for all $|z| \geq \overline{r}$.

Then for any $T > 0$, (6.2) possesses a nonconstant T periodic solution.

PROOF. Making the change of variables $\tau = 2\pi t T^{-1}$, (6.2) becomes

$$dz/d\tau = \lambda J H_z(z), \tag{6.11}$$

where $\lambda = (2\pi)^{-1}T$ and z is 2π periodic in τ. Since this has the same form as (6.2) with H replaced by λH, without loss of generality we can take $T = 2\pi$ and work with (6.2).

Basically the proof reduces to verifying that Theorem 5.29 is applicable here. However there are some technical complications. Since the growth condition (6.8) has not been assumed for H, the corresponding term in (6.9) need not belong to $C^1(E, \mathbf{R})$. Thus to get a C^1 functional on E, H will be modified so that it grows like a power of $|z|$ as $|z| \to \infty$. Let $K > 0$ and $\chi \in C^\infty(\mathbf{R}, \mathbf{R})$ such that $\chi(y) \equiv 1$ if $y \leq K$, $\chi(y) \equiv 0$ if $y \geq K+1$, and $\chi'(y) < 0$ if $y \in (K, K+1)$, where K is free for now. Set

$$H_K(z) \equiv \chi(|z|)H(z) + (1 - \chi(|z|))R|z|^4, \tag{6.12}$$

where $R = R(K)$ satisfies

$$R \geq \max_{K \leq |z| \leq K+1} \frac{H(z)}{|z|^4}.$$

Then $H_K \in C^1(\mathbf{R}^{2n}, \mathbf{R})$, satisfies (H_1)–(H_2) and (6.8) with $s = 4$. Moreover a straightforward computation shows (H_3) holds with μ replaced by $\nu = \min(\mu, 4)$. Integrating this inequality then yields

$$H_K(z) \geq a_3|z|^\nu - a_4 \tag{6.13}$$

for all $z \in \mathbf{R}^{2n}$, where $a_3, a_4 > 0$ and are *independent* of K. Finally set

$$I_K(z) = A(z) - \int_0^{2\pi} H_K(z)\,dt. \tag{6.14}$$

We will show I_K satisfies the hypotheses of Theorem 5.29. This will lead to a nonconstant 2π periodic (weak) solution $z_K(t)$ of

$$\dot{z} = JH_{Kz}(z). \tag{6.15}$$

It will then be shown that z_K is a classical solution of (6.15). Further estimates then prove there is a K_0 such that for all $K > K_0$, $\|z_K\|_{L^\infty} \le K_0$. Therefore $H_K(z_K) = H(z_K)$. Hence for such K, z_K satisfies (6.2).

Turning to a study of (6.14), by Proposition B.39, $I_K \in C^1(E, \mathbf{R})$. Choosing $E_1 \equiv E^+$ and $E_2 \equiv E^0 \oplus E^-$, we see that I_K satisfies (I_5) of Theorem 5.29 with L_i defined by

$$(L_i z, \varsigma) = A'(z)\varsigma$$

for $z \in E_i$ and

$$b(z) = -\int_0^{2\pi} H_K(z)\,dt.$$

Proposition B.39 implies that $b'(z)$ is compact. Hence (I_6) holds. The next three lemmas establish (I_7).

LEMMA 6.16. *If H satisfies (H_2), (I_7)(i) holds for I_K.*

PROOF. By (H_2), for any $\varepsilon > 0$, there is a $\delta > 0$ such that $H_K(z) \le \varepsilon|z|^2$ if $|z| \le \delta$. Since $H_K(z)|z|^{-4}$ is uniformly bounded as $|z| \to \infty$, there is an $M = M(\varepsilon, K)$ such that $H_K(z) \le M|z|^4$ for $|z| \ge \delta$. Hence

$$H_K(z) \le \varepsilon|z|^2 + M|z|^4 \tag{6.17}$$

for all $z \in \mathbf{R}^{2n}$. Therefore by (6.17) and Proposition 6.6,

$$\int_0^{2\pi} H_K(z)\,dt \le \varepsilon\|z\|_{L^2}^2 + M\|z\|_{L^4}^4 \le (\varepsilon\alpha_2 + M\alpha_4\|z\|^2)\|z\|^2. \tag{6.18}$$

Consequently for $z \in E_1 = E^+$,

$$I_K(z) \ge \|z\|^2 - (\varepsilon\alpha_2 + M\alpha_4\|z\|^2)\|z\|^2.$$

Choose $\varepsilon = (3\alpha_2)^{-1}$ and ρ so that $3M\alpha_4\rho^2 = 1$. Then for $z \in \partial B_\rho \cap E_1$,

$$I_K(z) \ge \tfrac{1}{3}\rho^2 \equiv \alpha.$$

Hence I_K satisfies (I_7)(i) with $S = \partial B_\rho \cap E_1$.

REMARK 6.19. ρ and α depend on K through M.

LEMMA 6.20. *If H satisfies (H_1) and (H_3), then I_K satisfies (I_7)(ii).*

PROOF. Let $e \in \partial B_1 \cap E_1$ and set

$$Q \equiv \{re \mid 0 \le r \le r_1\} \oplus (B_{r_2} \cap E_2),$$

where r_1 and r_2 are free for the moment. Define $\tilde{E} \equiv \text{span}\{e\} \oplus E_2$ so $Q \subset \tilde{E}$. Let $z = z^0 + z^- \in B_{r_2} \cap E_2$. Then

$$I_K(z+re) = r^2 - \|z^-\|^2 - \int_0^{2\pi} H_K(z+re)\,dt. \tag{6.21}$$

Now by simple inequalities and orthogonalities:

$$\begin{aligned} \int_0^{2\pi} H_K(z+re)\,dt &\geq a_3 \int_0^{2\pi} |z+re|^\nu\,dt - 2\pi a_4 \\ &\geq a_5 \left(\int_0^{2\pi} |z+re|^2\,dt \right)^{\nu/2} - a_6 \\ &= a_5 \left(\int_0^{2\pi} (|z^0|^2 + |z^-|^2 + r^2|e|^2)\,dt \right)^{\nu/2} - a_6 \\ &\geq a_7(|z^0|^\nu + r^\nu) - a_6. \end{aligned} \tag{6.22}$$

Combining (6.21)–(6.22) shows

$$I_K(z+re) \leq r^2 - \|z^-\|^2 - a_7(|z^0|^\nu + r^\nu) + a_6. \tag{6.23}$$

Choose r_1 so that

$$\varphi(r) \equiv r^2 - a_7 r^\nu + a_6 \leq 0 \tag{6.24}$$

for all $r \geq r_1$. Set

$$M = \max_{r \in [0, r_1]} \varphi(r).$$

Since

$$\psi(z) \equiv \|z^-\|^2 + a_7|z^0|^\nu \to \infty$$

uniformly as $\|z\| \to \infty$, in E_2, $\psi(z) \geq M$ if $\|z\|$ is large enough, e.g. $\|z\| \geq r_2$. Therefore by (6.23), if $\|z\| \geq r_2$,

$$I_K(z+re) \leq M - \psi(z) \leq 0. \tag{6.25}$$

Combining (6.24) and (6.25) with the fact that $I_K \leq 0$ on E_2 via (H_1), we see $I_K \leq 0 \equiv \omega$ on ∂Q and (I_7)(ii) holds.

REMARK 6.26. Both r_1 and r_2 and therefore Q are independent of K.

LEMMA 6.27. *If S and Q are defined as in Lemmas* 6.16 *and* 6.20, *then S and ∂Q link, i.e. I_K satisfies* (I_7)(iii).

PROOF. Immediate from the definitions of S and Q and Example 5.26.

The above three lemmas show I_K satisfies (I_7). Now to be able to use Theorem 5.28, it only remains to verify that I_K satisfies (PS). Thus suppose $|I_K(z_m)| \leq M$ and $I'_K(z_m) \to 0$ as $m \to \infty$. Then for large m and $z = z_m$:

$$\begin{aligned} M + \|z\| &\geq I_K(z) - \tfrac{1}{2} I'_K(z) z = \textstyle\int_0^{2\pi} [\tfrac{1}{2} z \cdot H_{Kz}(z) - H_K(z)]\,dt \\ &\geq (2^{-1} - \nu^{-1}) \int_0^{2\pi} z \cdot H_{Kz}(z)\,dt - M_1 \geq M_2 \|z\|_{L^4}^4 - M_3 \end{aligned} \tag{6.28}$$

via (H_3) and the form of H_K. In (6.28), both M_2 and M_3 depend on K. Writing $z = z^0 + z^+ + z^-$, (H_3) and simple estimates show

$$\begin{aligned} M + \|z\| &\geq (2^{-1} - \nu^{-1})\nu \int_0^{2\pi} H_K(z)\,dt - M_4 \\ &\geq M_5\|z\|_{L^\nu}^\nu - M_6 \geq M_7\|z\|_{L^2}^\nu - M_6 \geq 2\pi M_7|z^0|^\nu - M_6. \end{aligned} \tag{6.29}$$

Note that M_6 and M_7 are independent of K via (6.13). Inequality (6.29) can also be written as

$$|z^0| \leq M_8(1 + \|z\|^{\nu^{-1}}). \tag{6.30}$$

Next taking $z = z_m$ and $\varsigma = z_m^+$ in

$$|I_K'(z)\varsigma| = \left|A'(z)\varsigma - \int_0^{2\pi} H_{Kz}(z)\cdot\varsigma\,dt\right| \leq \|\varsigma\| \tag{6.31}$$

and using the Hölder inequality and (6.7) yields

$$\begin{aligned} 2\|z^+\|^2 = A'(z)z^+ &\leq \left|\int_0^{2\pi} H_{Kz}(z)z^+\,dt\right| + \|z^+\| \\ &\leq M_9(\|z\|_{L^4}^3 + 1)\|z^+\|. \end{aligned}$$

Hence

$$\|z^+\| \leq M_{10}(\|z\|_{L^4}^3 + 1) \leq M_{11}(\|z\|^{3/4} + 1) \tag{6.32}$$

via (6.28). Similarly choosing $\varsigma = -z^-$ in (6.31) yields (6.32) with z^+ replaced by z^-. Combining these inequalities with (6.30) shows

$$\|z\| \leq M_{12}(1 + \|z\|^{3/4} + \|z\|^{\nu^{-1}}) \tag{6.33}$$

which implies that (z_m) is bounded in E. To show that (z_m) is precompact in E, note that

$$\|z_m\|^2 = |z_m^0|^2 + \|z_m^+\|^2 + \|z_m^-\|^2.$$

Since E^0 is finite dimensional, (z_m^0) is precompact. By the argument of Proposition B.35,

$$\pm P^\pm I_K'(z) = z^\pm + T^\pm(z), \tag{6.34}$$

where $P^\pm$ is the orthogonal projector of E onto $E^\pm$ and $T^\pm(z)$ is compact. Hence (6.34) and $I_K'(z_m) \to 0$ as $m \to \infty$ implies (z_m) has a convergent subsequence.

Theorem 5.29 is now applicable and from it we conclude that I_K possesses a critical value $c_K \geq \alpha = \alpha(K) > 0$ with a corresponding critical point $z_K = (p_K, q_K)$. It remains to show that z_K is a classical nonconstant solution of (6.2). Since $I_K'(z_K)\varsigma = 0$ for all $\varsigma \in E$, choosing $\varsigma = (\varphi, \psi) \in W^{1,2}(S^1, \mathbf{R}^{2n})$ shows

$$\int_0^{2\pi} [p_K \cdot \dot{\psi} - q_K \cdot \dot{\varphi} - H_{Kz}(z_K)\cdot\varsigma]\,dt = 0. \tag{6.35}$$

In particular if $\varsigma \equiv 1$, (6.35) implies

$$\frac{1}{2\pi}\int_0^{2\pi} H_{Kz}(z_K)\,dt \equiv [H_{Kz}(z_K)] = 0 = [JH_{Kz}(z_K)].$$

Fourier expansion shows that if $y \in L^2(S^1, \mathbf{R}^{2n})$, $[y] = 0$, and $\xi \in \mathbf{R}^{2n}$, then there exists a unique $x \in W^{1,2}(S^1, \mathbf{R}^{2n})$ such that $[x] = \xi$ and $\dot{x} = y$. The choice of H_K and Proposition 6.6 show that $H_{Kz}(z_K) \in L^2(S^1, \mathbf{R}^{2n})$. Consequently choosing $y = \mathcal{J}H_{Kz}(z_K)$ and $\xi = [z_K]$, there is a unique $z = (p, q) \in W^{1,2}(S^1, \mathbf{R}^{2n})$ such that $[z] = [z_K]$ and

$$\dot{z} = \mathcal{J}H_{Kz}(z_K). \tag{6.36}$$

Taking the inner product of (6.36) with $\mathcal{J}\varsigma$, where $\varsigma = (\varphi, \psi) \in W^{1,2}(S^1, \mathbf{R}^{2n})$ and integrating by parts yields

$$\int_0^{2\pi} [p \cdot \dot{\psi} - q \cdot \dot{\varphi} - H_{Kz}(z_K) \cdot \varsigma]\, dt = 0. \tag{6.37}$$

Comparing (6.35) and (6.37) which hold for all $\varsigma \in W^{1,2}(S^1, \mathbf{R}^{2n})$ shows $z = z_K \in W^{1,2}(S^1, \mathbf{R}^{2n})$ and z_K satisfies (6.15) in an a.e. sense. But $z_K \in W^{1,2}(S^1, \mathbf{R}^{2n})$ easily implies z_K is Hölder continuous of order $\frac{1}{2}$. Therefore $H_{Kz}(z_k) \in C(S^1, \mathbf{R}^{2n})$ and (6.15) tells us $z_K \in C^1(S^1, \mathbf{R}^{2n})$ and is a classical solution of (6.15). If $z_K \equiv \text{const}$,

$$I_K(z_K) = -\int_0^{2\pi} H_K(z_K)\, dt \le 0$$

via (H_1). But $I_K(z_K) \ge \alpha(K) > 0$ so z_K is a nonconstant solution of (6.15).

The last step in the proof is to show that there is a $K_0 > 0$ such that for all $K \ge K_0$, $\|z_K\|_{L^\infty} < K$. Then $H_{Kz}(z_K) = H_z(z_K)$ and we have the desired solution of (6.2). By Theorem 5.29 and in particular (5.38)

$$I_K(z_K) = c_K = \inf_{h \in \Gamma} \sup_{z \in Q} I_K(h(1, z)).$$

Since $h(t, z) \equiv z \in \Gamma$,

$$c_K \le \sup_{z \in Q} I_K(z) \tag{6.38}$$

with Q as defined in Lemma 6.20. By Remark 6.26, r_1 and r_2 are independent of K. Then for $z = re + z^0 + z^- \in Q$,

$$I_K(z) = r^2 - \|z^-\|^2 - \int_0^{2\pi} H_K(z)\, dt \le r_1^2 \tag{6.39}$$

via (H_1). Consequently by (6.38)–(6.39), $c_K \le r_1^2$ independently of K. As in (6.28), this implies

$$\begin{aligned} r_1^2 &\ge I_K(z_K) - \tfrac{1}{2} I_K'(z_K) z_K \\ &\ge (2^{-1} - \nu^{-1}) \int_0^{2\pi} z_K \cdot H_{Kz}(z_K)\, dt - M_1. \end{aligned} \tag{6.40}$$

Thus (6.40) provides a K independent upper bound for $\int_0^{2\pi} z_K \cdot H_{Kz}(z_K)\, dt$. By (H_3),

$$H_K(\varsigma) \le \nu^{-1} \varsigma \cdot H_{Kz}(\varsigma) + M_2 \tag{6.41}$$

for all $\varsigma \in \mathbf{R}^{2n}$. Choosing $\varsigma = z_K$, integrating (6.41) over $[0, 2\pi]$, and recalling that $H_K(z_K) \equiv \text{const}$ since z_K satisfies a Hamiltonian system, (6.41) yields

$$2\pi H_K(z_K) \le \nu^{-1} \int_0^{2\pi} (z_K \cdot H_{Kz}(z_K))\, dt + 2\pi M_2. \tag{6.42}$$

The right-hand side of (6.42) is bounded from above independently of K via our above remarks. Thus (6.42) and (6.13) yield a K independent L^∞ bound for z_K and the proof of Theorem 6.10 is complete.

REMARK 6.43. In interpreting Theorem 6.10, a caveat is in order. In its setting, given any $T > 0$, there exists a nonconstant solution of (6.2) having period T. However T may not be the minimal period of the solution which may be Tk^{-1} for some $k \in \mathbf{N}$, $k > 1$. Under further hypotheses on H, Ambrosetti and Mancini [**AM2**], Deng [**De**], and Ekeland and Hofer [**EH**] have proved there exists a solution having minimal period T for any $T > 0$.

An easy consequence of Theorem 6.10 is

COROLLARY 6.44. *Under the hypotheses of Theorem* 6.10, *there exist infinitely many distinct T periodic solutions of* (6.2).

PROOF. Theorem 6.10 provides one such solution, $z_1(t)$. Suppose its minimal period is Tk_1^{-1}. Apply Theorem 6.10 again with T replaced by $T(2k_1)^{-1}$ to get a nonconstant $T(2k_1)^{-1}$ periodic solution $z_2(t)$. Certainly z_2 is T periodic and it is distinct from z_1 since its minimal period is less than Tk_1^{-1}. Repeating this process produces a sequence of distinct nonconstant T periodic solutions of (6.2).

REMARK 6.45. There is a much stronger version of Theorem 6.10 [**R9**]: If $H \in C^1(\mathbf{R}^{2n}, \mathbf{R})$ and satisfies (H_3), then for any $R, T > 0$, there exists a T periodic solution z of (6.2) with $\|z\|_{L^\infty} > R$ (see also [**Be1**]). Simple examples show that T may not be the minimal period of the solution. E.g. suppose $n = 1$ and $H(z) = G(|z|^2)$, where G is smooth and monotone increasing. Then (6.2) becomes

$$\dot{p} = -2G'(|z|^2)q, \qquad \dot{q} = 2G'(|z|^2)p$$

and $G'(|z|^2) \equiv \text{const}$ for a solution. Setting $\varsigma = p + iq$, ς satisfies

$$\dot{\varsigma} = 2iG'(|\varsigma|^2)\varsigma$$

so $\varsigma(t) = \varsigma_0 \exp(2iG'(|\varsigma|^2)t)$. Therefore if T is the minimal period, $T = \pi(G'(|\varsigma|^2))^{-1}$. In particular if $G' \ge 1$, $T \le \pi$.

We conclude this chapter with an application of a seemingly different nature. Consider (6.2) where instead of fixing the period, the energy is prescribed, e.g. $H(z) \equiv 1$.

THEOREM 6.46 [**R6**]. *Suppose $H \in C^1(\mathbf{R}^{2n}, \mathbf{R})$ and $H^{-1}(1)$ is the boundary of a compact starshaped neighborhood of* 0 *with $z \cdot H_z \ne 0$ on $H^{-1}(1)$. Then* (6.2) *has a periodic solution on $H^{-1}(1)$.*

This theorem will be obtained with the aid of Theorem 6.10. First a technical result.

PROPOSITION 6.47. *Suppose* $H, \overline{H} \in C^1(\mathbf{R}^{2n}, \mathbf{R})$ *with* $H^{-1}(1) = \overline{H}^{-1}(1)$ *and* $H_z, \overline{H}_z \neq 0$ *on* $H^{-1}(1)$. *If* $\varsigma(t)$ *satisfies*

$$\dot{\varsigma} = \mathcal{J}\overline{H}_z(\varsigma) \tag{6.48}$$

and $\varsigma(0) \in H^{-1}(1)$, *then there exists a reparametrization* $z(t)$ *of* $\varsigma(t)$ *such that* z *satisfies* (6.2) *and* $z(t) \in H^{-1}(1)$. *In particular if* ς *is periodic, so is* z.

PROOF. Since $H^{-1}(1)$ is a level set for H and $\overline{H}$ and $H_z, \overline{H}_z \neq 0$ on this set, these gradients must be proportional on $H^{-1}(1)$, i.e. there is a $\nu \in C(H^{-1}(1), \mathbf{R} \setminus \{0\})$ such that $H_z(z) = \nu(z)\overline{H}_z(z)$. Now $\varsigma(0) \in H^{-1}(1)$ and (6.48) is a Hamiltonian system so $\varsigma(t) \in H^{-1}(1)$. Set $z(t) \equiv \varsigma(r(t))$ where $r(0) = 0$ and r is a solution of

$$\dot{r} = \nu(\varsigma(r(t))). \tag{6.49}$$

Therefore z satisfies $z(0) = \varsigma(0) \in H^{-1}(1)$ and

$$\dot{z} = \frac{d\varsigma}{dr}\dot{r} = \nu(\varsigma(r(t)))\mathcal{J}\overline{H}_z(\varsigma(r(t))) = \mathcal{J}H_z(z(t)),$$

i.e. (6.2).

To justify the assertion about the periodic case, more care must be taken since the solution of (6.49) with $r(0) = 0$ may not be unique if ν is merely continuous. Suppose ς is T periodic and without loss of generality assume $\nu > 0$. Then $\nu > 0$ on $\varsigma([0, T])$ and (6.49) implies there is a first positive value $\bar{t}$ of t such that $r(\bar{t}) = T$. Set $s(t) = r(t)$ for $t \in [0, \bar{t}]$, and for $j \in \mathbf{N}$, set $s(t) = jT + r(t - j\bar{t})$ for $t \in [j\bar{t}, (j+1)\bar{t}]$. Then $s \in C^1$. Indeed we need only check what happens at $t = \bar{t}$.

$$\begin{aligned}
\lim_{t\uparrow\bar{t}} s'(t) &= \lim_{t\uparrow\bar{t}} r'(t) = \lim_{t\uparrow\bar{t}} \nu(\varsigma(r(t))) \\
&= \nu(\varsigma(T)) = \nu(\varsigma(0)) = \lim_{t\downarrow\bar{t}} \nu(\varsigma(r(t - \bar{t}))) \\
&= \lim_{t\downarrow\bar{t}} r'(t - \bar{t}) = \lim_{t\downarrow\bar{t}} s'(t).
\end{aligned}$$

It follows that $z(t) = \varsigma(s(t))$ is $\bar{t}$ periodic.

PROOF OF THEOREM 6.46. By Proposition 6.47, it suffices to find an $\overline{H}$ such that $\overline{H}^{-1}(1) = H^{-1}(1)$ and for which the existence of a periodic solution of (6.48) can be established. The geometrical assumption on $H^{-1}(1)$ leads to the construction of such a function. By the starshaped assumption for each $z \in \mathbf{R}^{2n}$, there is a unique $w(z) \in H^{-1}(1)$ and $\alpha(z) > 0$ such that $z = \alpha(z)w(z)$. Indeed $\alpha(z) = |z|\,|w(z)|^{-1}$. Note that α is homogeneous of degree one and is C^1 for $z \neq 0$. Define $\overline{H}(0) = 0$ and $\overline{H}(z) = \alpha(z)^4$ for $z \neq 0$. Then $\overline{H} \in C^1(\mathbf{R}^{2n}, \mathbf{R})$, $\overline{H}^{-1}(1) = H^{-1}(1)$, $\overline{H} \geq 0$, $\overline{H}(z) = o(|z|^2)$ as $|z| \to 0$, and $z\cdot\overline{H}_z(z) = 4\overline{H}(z)$ since $\overline{H}$ is homogeneous of degree 4. Thus $\overline{H}$ satisfies all of the hypotheses of Theorem 6.10. Hence for e.g. $T = 2\pi$, there exists a nonconstant 2π periodic solution ς of (6.48). It need not be the case that $\overline{H}(\varsigma(t)) \equiv 1$. However $\overline{H}(\varsigma(t)) \equiv \beta \neq 0$ since $\varsigma \not\equiv 0$. Set $\gamma = \beta^{-1/4}$. Therefore $\overline{H}(\gamma\varsigma) \equiv 1$. Moreover

$$(\gamma\dot{\varsigma}) = \gamma\mathcal{J}\overline{H}_z(\varsigma) = \gamma^{-2}\mathcal{J}\overline{H}_z(\gamma\varsigma) \tag{6.50}$$

via the homogeneity of $\overline{H}_z$. Finally let $t = \gamma^2\tau$ and $z(\tau) = \gamma\varsigma(t)$. Then z is $2\pi\gamma^{-2}$ periodic and by (6.50) satisfies

$$\frac{dz}{d\tau} = \gamma^{-2}\mathcal{J}\overline{H}_z(\gamma\varsigma)\frac{dt}{d\tau} = \mathcal{J}\overline{H}_z(z).$$

Thus z is the desired solution and the proof is complete.

REMARK 6.51. It is possible to make a more direct study of the existence and multiplicity of periodic solutions of (6.2) having prescribed energy using a direct variational approach and ideas from Chapters 7–9. See e.g. [**AM1**, **BLMR**, **EL**, **VG**, **W**].

7. Functionals with Symmetries and Index Theories

Probably the most striking applications of minimax methods are results which establish the existence of multiple critical points of functionals which are invariant under a group of symmetries. In this chapter some machinary to treat such questions will be introduced. To be a bit more precise, let E be a real Banach space, $\mathcal{G}$ a group of mappings of E into E, and $I \in C^1(E, \mathbf{R})$. We say I is *invariant* under $\mathcal{G}$ if $I(gu) = I(u)$ for all $g \in \mathcal{G}$ and $u \in E$. As a simple example, suppose I is even, i.e. $I(u) = I(-u)$ for all $u \in E$. Then I is invariant under $\mathcal{G} = \{\text{id}, -\text{id}\} \simeq \mathbf{Z}_2$. As was noted in Chapter 1, a second example is provided by (1.7), a functional associated with periodic solutions of Hamiltonian systems where $\mathcal{G} \simeq S^1$.

The earliest multiplicity result for symmetric functionals is due to Ljusternik and Schnirelmann who proved [**LLS**]:

THEOREM 7.1. *If $I \in C^1(E, \mathbf{R})$ and is even, then $I|_{S^{m-1}}$ has at least m distinct pairs of critical points.*

In order to prove Theorem 7.1 or other such results, we need a tool to measure the "size" of a symmetric set. (By a symmetric set, we mean one which is invariant under the symmetry group.) The so-called *Ljusternik-Schnirelmann category* [**LLS**] was introduced for this purpose. A simpler notion, that of *genus*, is easier to deal with and will be used here. Genus is due to Krasnoselski [**K**] although we will use an equivalent definition due to Coffman [**Co1**] (see also [**CF**]).

Let E be a real Banach space and let $\mathcal{E}$ denote the family of sets $A \subset E \setminus \{0\}$ such that A is closed in E and symmetric with respect to 0, i.e. $x \in A$ implies $-x \in A$. For $A \in \mathcal{E}$, define the genus of A to be n (denoted by $\gamma(A) = n$) if there is an odd map $\varphi \in C(A, \mathbf{R}^n \setminus \{0\})$ and n is the smallest integer with this property. When there does not exist a finite such n, set $\gamma(A) = \infty$. Finally set $\gamma(\emptyset) = 0$.

EXAMPLE 7.2. Suppose $B \subset E$ is closed and $B \cap (-B) = \emptyset$. Let $A = B \cup (-B)$. Then $\gamma(A) = 1$ since the function $\varphi(x) = 1$ for $x \in B$ and $\varphi(x) = -1$ for $x \in -B$ is odd and lies in $C(A, \mathbf{R} \setminus \{0\})$.

REMARK 7.3. If $A \in \mathcal{E}$ and $\gamma(A) > 1$, then A contains infinitely many distinct points, for if A were finite we could write $A = B \cup (-B)$ with B as in Example 7.2. But then $\gamma(A) = 1$.

EXAMPLE 7.4. If $n \geq 1$ and A is homeomorphic to S^n by an odd map, then $\gamma(A) > 1$. Otherwise there is a mapping $\varphi \in C(A, \mathbf{R} \setminus \{0\})$ with φ odd. Choose any $x \in A$ such that $\varphi(x) > 0$. Then $\varphi(-x) < 0$ and by the Intermediate Value Theorem, φ must vanish somewhere on any path in A joining x and $-x$, a contradiction.

The main properties of genus will be listed in the next proposition. For $A \in \mathcal{E}$ and $\delta > 0$, let $N_\delta(A)$ denote a uniform δ-neighborhood of A, i.e. $N_\delta(A) = \{x \in E |\, \|x - A\| \leq \delta\}$.

PROPOSITION 7.5. *Let $A, B \in \mathcal{E}$. Then*

1° *Normalization: If $x \neq 0$, $\gamma(\{x\} \cup \{-x\}) = 1$.*

2° *Mapping property: If there exists an odd map $f \in C(A, B)$, then $\gamma(A) \leq \gamma(B)$.*

3° *Monotonicity property: If $A \subset B$, $\gamma(A) \leq \gamma(B)$.*

4° *Subadditivity: $\gamma(A \cup B) \leq \gamma(A) + \gamma(B)$.*

5° *Continuity property: If A is compact, $\gamma(A) < \infty$ and there is a $\delta > 0$ such that $N_\delta(A) \in \mathcal{E}$ and $\gamma(N_\delta(A)) = \gamma(A)$.*

PROOF. 1° is a special case of Example 7.2. To prove 2°–5° we assume that $\gamma(A), \gamma(B) < \infty$; the remaining cases are trivial. For 2°, suppose $\gamma(B) = n$. Then there exists a function φ belonging to $C(B, \mathbf{R}^n \setminus \{0\})$. Consequently $\varphi \circ f$ is odd and in $C(A, \mathbf{R}^n \setminus \{0\})$. Therefore $\gamma(A) \leq n = \gamma(B)$. Choosing $f = \mathrm{id}$ in 2° yields 3°. For 4°, suppose $\gamma(A) = m$ and $\gamma(B) = n$. Then there exist mappings $\varphi \in C(A, \mathbf{R}^m \setminus \{0\})$ and $\psi \in C(B, \mathbf{R}^n \setminus \{0\})$, both odd. By the Tietze Extension Theorem, there are mappings $\hat{\varphi} \in C(E, \mathbf{R}^m)$ and $\hat{\psi} \in C(E, \mathbf{R}^n)$ such that $\hat{\varphi}|_A = \varphi$ and $\hat{\psi}|_B = \psi$. Replacing $\hat{\varphi}, \hat{\psi}$ by their odd parts, we can assume $\hat{\varphi}, \hat{\psi}$ are odd. Set $f = (\hat{\varphi}, \hat{\psi})$. Then $f \in C(A \cup B, \mathbf{R}^{m+n} \setminus \{0\})$ and is odd. Therefore $\gamma(A \cup B) \leq m + n = \gamma(A) + \gamma(B)$. Lastly to get 5°, for each $x \in A$, set $r(x) \equiv \frac{1}{2}\|x\| = r(-x)$ and $T_x = B_{r(x)}(x) \cup B_{r(x)}(-x)$. Then $\gamma(\overline{T}_x) = 1$ by Example 7.2. Certainly $A \subset \bigcup_{x \in A} T_x$ and by the compactness of A, $A \subset \bigcup_{i=1}^k T_{x_i}$ for some finite set of points $x_1, \ldots, x_k$. Therefore $\gamma(A) < \infty$ via 4°. If $\gamma(A) = n$, there is a mapping $\varphi \in C(A, \mathbf{R}^n \setminus \{0\})$ with φ odd. Extend φ to an odd function $\hat{\varphi}$ as in 4°. Since A is compact, there is a $\delta > 0$ such that $\hat{\varphi} \neq 0$ on $N_\delta(A)$. Therefore $\gamma(N_\delta(A)) \leq n = \gamma(A)$. But by 3°, $\gamma(A) \leq \gamma(N_\delta(A))$ so we have equality.

REMARK 7.6. For later arguments it is useful to observe that if $\gamma(B) < \infty$, $\gamma(\overline{A \setminus B}) \geq \gamma(A) - \gamma(B)$. Indeed $A \subset \overline{A \setminus B} \cup B$ so the inequality follows from 3°–4° of Proposition 7.5.

Next we will calculate the genus of an important class of sets.

PROPOSITION 7.7. *If $A \subset E$, Ω is a bounded neighborhood of 0 in $\mathbf{R}^k$, and there exists a mapping $h \in C(A, \partial\Omega)$ with h an odd homeomorphism, then $\gamma(A) = k$.*

PROOF. Plainly $\gamma(A) \leq k$. If $\gamma(A) = j < k$, there is a $\varphi \in C(A, \mathbf{R}^j \setminus \{0\})$ with φ odd. Then $\varphi \circ h^{-1}$ is odd and belongs to $C(\partial\Omega, \mathbf{R}^j \setminus \{0\})$. But this is contrary to the Borsuk-Ulam Theorem [**S2**] since $k > j$. Therefore $\gamma(A) = k$.

The next result illustrates how symmetry provides us with a tool for obtaining intersection theorems.

PROPOSITION 7.8 [**C1**]. *Let X be a subspace of E of codimension k and $A \in \mathcal{E}$ with $\gamma(A) > k$. Then $A \cap X \neq \emptyset$.*

PROOF. Writing $E = V \oplus X$ with V a k dimensional complement of X, let P denote the projector of E onto V. If $A \cap X = \emptyset$, $P \in C(A, V \setminus \{0\})$. Moreover P is odd. Hence by 2° of Proposition 7.5, $\gamma(A) \leq \gamma(PA)$. The radial projection of PA into $\partial B_1 \cap V$ is another continuous odd map. Hence $\gamma(A) \leq \gamma(\partial B_1 \cap V) = k$ via Proposition 7.7, contrary to hypothesis.

As was mentioned earlier, there are other ways in which to measure the size of symmetric sets, not only in a $\mathbf{Z}_2$ setting but for more general group actions. Suppose E is a real Banach space with a group $\mathcal{G}$ acting on it. Set

$$\operatorname{Fix} \mathcal{G} \equiv \{u \in E | gu = u \text{ for all } g \in \mathcal{G}\}.$$

E.g. for $\mathcal{G} = \{\mathrm{id}, -\mathrm{id}\}$, $\operatorname{Fix} \mathcal{G} = \{0\}$ while for the Hamiltonian example (1.7), $\operatorname{Fix} \mathcal{G}$ consists of the set of $2n$ tuples of constant vectors. Let $\mathcal{E}$ denote the family of invariant subsets of $E \setminus \{0\}$, i.e. $A \in \mathcal{E}$ if $gx \in A$ for all $g \in \mathcal{G}$ and $x \in A$. We say we have an *index theory* for $(E, \mathcal{G})$ if there is a mapping $i\colon \mathcal{E} \to \mathbf{N} \cup \{\infty\}$ such that for all $A, B \in \mathcal{E}$,

1° *Normalization*: If $x \notin \operatorname{Fix} \mathcal{G}$, $i(\bigcup_{g \in \mathcal{G}} gx) = 1$.

2° *Mapping property*: If $f \in C(A, B)$ and f is equivariant, i.e. $fg = gf$ for all $g \in \mathcal{G}$, then $i(A) \leq i(B)$.

3° *Monotonicity property*: If $A \subset B$, $i(A) \leq i(B)$.

4° *Subadditivity*: $i(A \cup B) \leq i(A) + i(B)$.

5° *Continuity property*: If A is compact and $A \cap \operatorname{Fix} \mathcal{G} = \emptyset$, then $i(A) < \infty$ and there is a $\delta > 0$ such that $N_\delta(A) \in \mathcal{E}$ and $i(N_\delta(A)) = i(A)$.

REMARK 7.9. If $A \in \mathcal{E}$ and $A \cap \operatorname{Fix} \mathcal{G} \neq \emptyset$, then $i(A) = \sup_{B \in \mathcal{E}} i(B)$. Indeed let $x \in A \cap \operatorname{Fix} \mathcal{G}$ and define $f\colon A \to \{x\}$ via $f(u) = x$ for all $u \in A$. This map is continuous and equivariant. Hence $i(A) \leq i(\{x\}) \leq i(A)$ via the mapping and monotonicity properties of i. But A can be replaced by $\overline{E \setminus B_r(0)}$ for e.g. $r < \frac{1}{2}\|x\|$ and any $B \in \mathcal{E}$ lies in such a set.

The genus, γ, provides us with a simple index theory where $\mathcal{G} = \{\mathrm{id}, -\mathrm{id}\}$. As to other index theories, Benci has introduced an S^1 version of genus [**Be**]. Cohomological index theories can be found e.g. in [**Y**, **FR1–2**, **FHR**] and the references cited there. E.g. an especially general such situation is contained in Fadell-Husseini [**FH**]. One can also find analogues of Propositions 7.7–7.8 for these theories.

In the next two chapters we shall see how these tools can be used to obtain multiplicity results for symmetric functionals.

8. Multiple Critical Points of Symmetric Functionals: Problems with Constraints

The following two chapters study the existence of multiple critical points of functionals possessing a $\mathbf{Z}_2$ symmetry. The same ideas together with an appropriate index theory can be used to treat other kinds of symmetries. See e.g. [**AZ, Be2–3, BF, Bg, Br1–2, Pa1–2, S1–2**]. Theorem 1.10, the classical result of Ljusternik and Schnirelmann [**LLS**] is for a constrained functional, i.e. a functional on a manifold. In this chapter we will prove that result as well as an infinite dimensional generalization and give an application to (2.31). Chapter 9 treats unconstrained functionals. For either type of problem, the main difficulty is to find an appropriate class of sets with respect to which one can minimax the functional. We will see how this can be done in the constrained setting first, following Ljusternik and Schnirelmann. For convenience we restate their result:

THEOREM 8.1. *Suppose $I \in C^1(\mathbf{R}^n, \mathbf{R})$ and is even. Then $I|_{S^{n-1}}$ possesses at least n distinct pairs of critical points.*

PROOF. For $E = \mathbf{R}^n$ and $1 \le j \le n$, define

$$\gamma_j = \{A \in \mathcal{E} \,|\, A \subset S^{n-1} \text{ and } \gamma(A) \ge j\}. \tag{8.2}$$

This family of sets possesses the following properties:

(8.3)

1° $\gamma_j \ne \varnothing, 1 \le j \le n.$

2° *Monotonicity property*: $\gamma_1 \supset \gamma_2 \supset \cdots \supset \gamma_n$.

3° *Invariance property*: Suppose $\varphi \in C(S^{n-1}, S^{n-1})$ and is odd. Then $\varphi\colon \gamma_j \to \gamma_j$, i.e. $\varphi(A) \in \gamma_j$ whenever $A \in \gamma_j$.

4° *Excision property*: If $A \in \gamma_j$ and $B \in \mathcal{E}$ with $\gamma(B) \le s < j$, then $\overline{A \setminus B} \in \gamma_{j-s}$.

Indeed 1° follows from Proposition 7.7 with $\Omega = S^{n-1}$, 2° is trivial, 3° is a consequence of the mapping property of Proposition 7.5, and 4° follows from Remark 7.6.

Define

$$c_j = \inf_{A \in \gamma_j} \max_{u \in A} I(u), \qquad 1 \le j \le n. \tag{8.4}$$

From the monotonicity property of the γ_j, it is clear that $c_1 \le c_2 \le \cdots \le c_n$. We will show that c_j is a critical value of $I|_{S^{n-1}}$. This fact in itself is not sufficient to prove Theorem 8.1 since some of the minimax values may coincide with only one corresponding critical point. The following proposition together with Remark 7.3 shows the c_j's are critical values and we get enough corresponding critical points. Note that $I|'_{S^{n-1}}(u) = I'(u) - \lambda u$, where $\lambda = (I'(u), u)$.

PROPOSITION 8.5. *If* $c_j = \cdots = c_{j+p} \equiv c$, *and* $\hat{K}_c = \{x \in S^{n-1} | I(x) = c$ *and* $I|'_{S^{n-1}}(x) = 0\}$, *then* $\gamma(\hat{K}_c) \ge p + 1$.

PROOF. Suppose that $\gamma(\hat{K}_c) \le p$. Then by 5° of Proposition 7.5, there is a $\delta > 0$ such that $\gamma(N_\delta(\hat{K}_c)) \le p$. Hence if $\hat{N} \equiv N_\delta(\hat{K}_c) \cap S^{n-1}$, by 3° of Proposition 7.5, $\gamma(\hat{N}) \le p$. Invoking Theorem A.4 and Remark A.17(iv) with $\mathcal{O} \equiv \operatorname{int} \hat{N}$ and $\bar{\varepsilon} = 1$, there is an $\varepsilon \in (0,1)$ and $\eta \in C([0,1] \times S^{n-1}, S^{n-1})$ with $\eta(t,u)$ odd in u and satisfying

$$\eta(1, \hat{A}_{c+\varepsilon} \setminus \hat{N}) \subset \hat{A}_{c-\varepsilon}. \tag{8.6}$$

Choose $A \in \gamma_{j+p}$ such that $\max_A I \le c + \varepsilon$. By 4° of (8.3), $\overline{A \setminus \hat{N}} \in \gamma_j$ and by 3° of (8.3), $\eta(1, \overline{A \setminus \hat{N}}) \in \gamma_j$. Therefore by (8.6) and the definition of c,

$$c \le \max_{\eta(1,\overline{A \setminus \hat{N}})} I \le c - \varepsilon,$$

a contradiction.

REMARKS 8.7. (i) The minimax values c_j can be given another more geometrical characterization, namely

$$c_j = \inf\{r \in \mathbf{R} | \gamma(\hat{A}_r) \ge j\}. \tag{8.8}$$

Thus the c_j's are just those numbers at which the sets $\hat{A}_r$ change genus. Indeed denote the right-hand side of (8.8) by $\bar{c}_j$. If $r > \bar{c}_j$, $\gamma(\hat{A}_r) \ge j$ so $\hat{A}_r \in \gamma_j$ and

$$c_j \le \max_{\hat{A}_r} I = r. \tag{8.9}$$

Thus (8.9) shows $c_j \le \bar{c}_j$. If $c_j < \bar{c}_j$, let $c = (c_j + \bar{c}_j)/2$. Then there is an $A \in \gamma_j$ such that $\max_A I \le c$. Therefore $\gamma(\hat{A}_c) \ge \gamma(A) \ge j$ by 3° of (8.3) but $c < \bar{c}_j$, a contradiction.

(ii) There are other ways to obtain critical values of $I|_{S^{-1}}$. E.g. define

$$b_k = \sup_{A \in \gamma_k} \min_{u \in A} I(u), \qquad 1 \le k \le n.$$

Clearly $b_1 \ge b_2 \ge \cdots \ge b_n$ and using Theorem A.4 and Remark A.17(iv) shows the b_k's are also critical values of $I|_{S^{n-1}}$. Note that $c_1 = \min_{S^{n-1}} I$ since if $x \in S^{n-1}$, $\{x\} \cup \{-x\} \in \gamma_1$. Moreover $c_1 = b_n$. To prove this, it suffices to show that $\gamma_n = \{S^{n-1}\}$. If not, there is a set $A \in \gamma_n$ such that $A \ne S^{n-1}$. Therefore there is a point $y \in S^{n-1} \setminus A$. Without loss of generality we can assume $y = (\hat{0}, 1)$ with $\hat{0}$ the origin in $\mathbf{R}^{n-1}$. The projection map $P(u) = (u_1, \ldots, u_{n-1}, 0)$ belongs to $C(A, \mathbf{R}^{n-1} \setminus \{0\})$ and is odd. Therefore by the argument of Proposition 7.8,

$\gamma(A) \le n-1$, a contradiction. Thus $c_1 = b_n$. Similarly $c_n = b_1 = \max_{S^{n-1}} I$. We do not know if $c_j = b_{n-j+1}$ if $j \ne 1, n$, However if one used the cohomological index theory of [**FR1**] instead of genus and defined corresponding minimax and maximin values c_j^*, b_j^*, it can be shown that $c_j^* = b_{n-j+1}^*$. Thus in this sense the cohomological index is a nicer tool to deal with.

There are many infinite dimensional generalizations of Theorem 8.1. E.g.

THEOREM 8.10. *Let E be an infinite dimensional Hilbert space and let $I \in C^1(E, \mathbf{R})$ be even. Suppose $r > 0$, $I|_{\partial B_r}$ satisfies (PS), and $I|_{\partial B_r}$ is bounded from below. Then $I|_{\partial B_r}$ possesses infinitely many distinct pairs of critical points.*

PROOF. Define the sets γ_j as in (8.2) for $j \in \mathbf{N}$ with S^{n-1} replaced by ∂B_r. These sets still satisfy properties 1°–4° (again with S^{n-1} replaced by ∂B_r). Now define

$$c_j = \inf_{A \in \Gamma_j} \sup_{u \in A} I(u), \qquad j \in \mathbf{N}. \tag{8.11}$$

Since $I|_{\partial B_r}$ is bounded from below, $c_1 > -\infty$. Moreover (PS) implies $\hat{K}_c \equiv \{u \in \partial B_r | I(u) = c \text{ and } I|'_{\partial B_r}(u) = 0\}$ is a compact set for any $c \in \mathbf{R}$. With these observations and Remark A.17(iv), the argument of Proposition 8.5 proves the theorem as earlier.

REMARK 8.12. The requirement that $I|_{\partial B_r}$ satisfies (PS) is too stringent a condition for applications. Consider e.g.

$$\begin{aligned} -\Delta u &= \lambda p(x,u), \qquad x \in \Omega, \\ u &= 0, \qquad x \in \partial\Omega, \end{aligned} \tag{8.13}$$

with Ω as usual. Suppose that p satisfies (p_1)–(p_2) and

(p_8') $\xi p(x,\xi) > 0$ if $\xi \ne 0$, and

(p_9) $p(x,\xi)$ is odd in ξ.

Let $E \equiv W_0^{1,2}(\Omega)$ and $u \in E$. Set

$$I(u) \equiv -\int_\Omega P(x,u)\,dx. \tag{8.14}$$

Then $I \in C^1(E, \mathbf{R})$ by Proposition B.10 and I is even. At a critical point u of $I|_{\partial B_1}$ we have

$$I'(u)\varphi - \mu(u,\varphi) = 0 = -\int_\Omega p(x,u)\varphi\,dx - \mu\int_\Omega \nabla u \cdot \nabla\varphi\,dx \tag{8.15}$$

for all $\varphi \in E$. Choosing $\varphi = u$ and using (p_8') shows

$$\mu = I'(u)u = -\int_\Omega p(x,u)u\,dx < 0.$$

Therefore u is a weak solution of (8.13) with $\lambda = -\mu^{-1}$. This suggests using Theorem 8.10 to get weak solutions of (8.13) on ∂B_1 (or ∂B_r).

To apply Theorem 8.8, observe first that by Proposition B.10, I is weakly continuous, i.e. $u_m \rightharpoonup u$ implies $I(u_m) \to I(u)$. This implies that $I|_{\partial B_1}$ is bounded from below for otherwise there is a sequence $(u_m) \subset \partial B_1$ such that $I(u_m) < -m$. But, being bounded, (u_m) has a subsequence converging weakly in E to $\overline{u} \in \overline{B_1}$. Hence $I(u_m) \to I(\overline{u}) = -\infty$ contrary to $I \in C^1(E, \mathbf{R})$.

To verify (PS), let (u_m) be any sequence in ∂B_1 such that $(I(u_m))$ is bounded and $I|'_{\partial B_1}(u_m) \to 0$ as $m \to \infty$, i.e.

$$I|'_{\partial B_1}(u_m) = I'(u_m) - (I'(u_m)u_m)u_m \to 0. \tag{8.16}$$

Since (u_m) is bounded in E and I' is compact (Proposition B.10), along some subsequence u_m converges weakly to some $u \in E$ and

$$I'(u_m) \to I'(u) - (I'(u)u)u = 0.$$

By the weak continuity of I, $I(u_m) \to I(u)$. If $I(u) \neq 0$, by (p_8'), $u \neq 0$. Hence $I'(u)u \neq 0$ and $I'(u_m)u_m \neq 0$ for large m. Consequently (8.16) shows

$$u_m = (I'(u_m)u_m)^{-1}(I|'_{\partial B_1}(u_m) - I'(u_m))$$

possesses a convergent subsequence. However if $I(u) = 0$, u_m need not have a convergent subsequence. In fact by the above argument any sequence (u_m) which is weakly convergent to 0 has $I(u_m) \to 0$ and $I|'_{\partial B_1}(u_m) \to 0$ but (u_m) does not necessarily have a convergent subsequence.

What we have actually shown above is that $I|_{\partial B_1}$ satisfies $(\mathrm{PS})_{\mathrm{loc}}$ for all $c \not\equiv 0$ where $(\mathrm{PS})_{\mathrm{loc}}$ is defined in Remark A.17(i). Moreover $(\mathrm{PS})_{\mathrm{loc}}$ at c is all we need for the proof of the Deformation Theorem. Thus Theorem 8.10 is also valid with (PS) replaced by $(\mathrm{PS})_{\mathrm{loc}}$ for each c_j defined by (8.11). To apply this result to (8.13), by the remarks just made, we need only verify that $c_j < 0$ for all j. But this is immediate from (p_8') and (8.11). Thus we have proved

THEOREM 8.17. *If p satisfies $(p_1), (p_2), (p_8')$, and (p_9),* (8.13) *possesses a sequence of distinct pairs of weak solutions $(\lambda_k, \pm u_k)$ on $\mathbf{R} \times \partial B_r$, where $\lambda_k = -(I'(u_k)u_k)^{-1}$.*

COROLLARY 8.18. *$c_k = I(u_k) \to 0$ as $k \to \infty$.*

PROOF. Let $v_1, \dots, v_k$ be as in (2.40) and set $E_k = \mathrm{span}\{v_1, \dots, v_k\}$ and $E_k^\perp$ its orthogonal complement. By Proposition 7.8, if $A \in \gamma_k$, $A \cap E_{k-1}^\perp \neq \emptyset$. Therefore

$$\sup_A I \geq \inf_{E_{k-1}^\perp \cap \partial B_r} I.$$

Consequently

$$c_k \geq \inf_{E_{k-1}^\perp \cap \partial B_r} I. \tag{8.19}$$

By (p_2)

$$|I(u)| \leq \int_\Omega (a_1|u|^{s+1} + a_2|u|)\, dx \leq a_1\|u\|_{L^{s+1}(\Omega)}^{s+1} + a_3\|u\|_{L^2(\Omega)}. \tag{8.20}$$

By the Gagliardo-Nirenberg inequality [**N1**], or [**Fr**],

$$\|u\|_{L(\Omega)}^{s+1} \le \alpha_s \left(\int_\Omega |\nabla u|^2\right)^{a/2} \left(\int_\Omega u^2\right)^{(1-a)/2}, \tag{8.21}$$

where $a \in (0,1)$ is defined by

$$\frac{1}{s+1} = a\left(\frac{1}{2} - \frac{1}{n}\right) + (1-a)\frac{1}{2}.$$

If $u \in E_{k-1}^{\perp}$,

$$\int_\Omega u^2\,dx \le \lambda_k^{-1} \int_\Omega |\nabla u|^2\,dx \tag{8.22}$$

as in (4.13). Combining (8.20)–(8.22) shows

$$|I(u)| \le a_4(\lambda_k^{-(1-a)(s+1)} + \lambda_k^{-1/2}) \tag{8.23}$$

for $u \in E_{k-1}^{\perp} \cap \partial B_1$. As is well known [**CH**], $\lambda_k \to \infty$ as $k \to \infty$. Hence (8.11), (8.19), (8.20), and (8.23) show $I(u_k) \to 0$ as $k \to \infty$.

9. Multiple Critical Points of Symmetric Functionals: The Unconstrained Case

This section contains two abstract results: Clark's Theorem and a symmetric version of the Mountain Pass Theorem as well as some applications of these results.

We begin with the following version of Clark's Theorem.

THEOREM 9.1 [**C**]. *Let E be a real Banach space, $I \in C^1(E, \mathbf{R})$ with I even, bounded from below, and satisfying (PS). Suppose $I(0) = 0$, there is a set $K \subset E$ such that K is homeomorphic to S^{j-1} by an odd map, and* $\sup_K I < 0$. *Then I possesses at least j distinct pairs of critical points.*

PROOF. We argue almost exactly as in Theorem 8.1. Let

$$\gamma_k \equiv \{A \in \mathcal{E} | \gamma(A) \geq k\}$$

and define

$$c_k = \inf_{A \in \gamma_k} \sup_{u \in A} I(u), \qquad 1 \leq k \leq j. \tag{9.2}$$

The sets γ_k satisfy properties $1°$–$4°$ of (8.3) with S^{n-1} replaced by E. Hence $c_1 \leq c_2 \leq \cdots \leq c_j$. Moreover $c_1 > -\infty$ since I is bounded from below and $c_j < 0$ since $\gamma(K) = j$ via Proposition 7.7 and $I|_K < 0$. The result now follows from:

PROPOSITION 9.3. *If $c_k = \cdots = c_{k+j} \equiv c$ and $K_c \equiv \{u \in E | I(u) = c$ and $I'(u) = 0\}$, then $\gamma(K_c) \geq p + 1$.*

PROOF. The proof follows almost the same lines as that of Proposition 8.3 and will be omitted. (Use must be made of the fact that $I(0) = 0$ and $c_i < 0$ for $1 \leq i \leq k$. Therefore $0 \notin K_{c_i}$ so $K_{c_i} \in \mathcal{E}$ and $\gamma(K_{c_i}) < \infty$ via (PS).)

REMARK 9.4. Actually in [**C**], Clark does not assume that I is bounded from below or that there is a K as above but merely that if c_k is defined as in (9.2), then $-\infty < c_k < 0$. The above proof then shows c_k is a critical value of I. The form of the special case given in Theorem 9.2 is perhaps more useful for applications.

Two such applications will be given next (see e.g. [**AR**, **He2**, and **R2**]). They are related to problems treated in Chapter 2, namely (2.31) and (2.39). Consider first

$$(9.5)\qquad \begin{aligned} -\Delta u &= \lambda(a(x)u - p(x,u)), \quad x \in \Omega,\\ u &= 0, \qquad x \in \partial\Omega, \end{aligned}$$

where Ω is as usual and p satisfies $(p_1'), (p_3)$,

(p_5') there is a $\xi_1 > 0$ such that $a(x)\xi_1 - p(x,\xi_1) \le 0$ for all $x \in \Omega$, and (p_9).

THEOREM 9.6. *Suppose* p *satisfies* $(p_1'), (p_3), (p_5'), (p_9)$, *and* $\lambda > \lambda_k$, *the* k*th eigenvalue of* (2.40). *Then* (9.5) *possesses at least* k *distinct pairs of nontrivial solutions.*

PROOF. We begin by modifying the problem in a familiar fashion,. For $x \in \overline{\Omega}$, set $q(x,\xi) = a(x)\xi - p(x,\xi)$ if $\xi \in [0,\xi_1]$, $q(x,\xi) = q(x,\xi_1)$ if $\xi > \xi_1$, and let q be odd in ξ. Consider

$$(9.7)\qquad \begin{aligned} -\Delta u &= \lambda q(x,u), \qquad x \in \Omega,\\ u &= 0, \qquad x \in \partial\Omega. \end{aligned}$$

Arguing as in the proof of Corollary 2.23 shows any solution of (9.7) is a solution of (9.5). Hence to prove Theorem 9.6, it suffices to produce at least k distinct pairs of critical points of

$$I(u) = \int_\Omega [\tfrac{1}{2}|\nabla u|^2 - \lambda Q(x,u)]\,dx,$$

where Q is the primitive of q and $E = W_0^{1,2}(\Omega)$ as usual. Since q satisfies (p_1') and is a bounded function, $I \in C^1(E,\mathbf{R})$ via Proposition B.10. Likewise I is bounded from below and (PS) holds as in the proof of Theorem 2.32. Clearly $I(0) = 0$ and I is even. Thus the proof of Theorem 9.6 follows from Theorem 9.1 once the existence of a set K as in that theorem has been established. Let $v_1,\dots,v_k$ denote the eigenfunctions of (2.40) corresponding to $\lambda_1,\dots,\lambda_k$ normalized so that

$$\|v_i\| = 1 = \lambda_i \int_\Omega v_i^2\,dx, \qquad 1 \le i \le k.$$

Set

$$(9.8)\qquad K \equiv \left\{ \sum_{i=1}^k \alpha_i v_i \,\middle|\, \sum \alpha_i^2 = r^2 \right\}.$$

It is clear that K is homeomorphic to S^{n-1} by an odd map for any $r > 0$. We claim $I|_K < 0$ if r is sufficiently small. Indeed for small r and $u \in K$, $|u(x)| \le \xi_1$ so $Q(u) = au^2/2 - P(x,u)$. Therefore by (p_3),

$$\begin{aligned} I(u) &= \frac{1}{2}\sum_{i=1}^k \alpha_i^2 - \frac{\lambda}{2}\sum_{i=1}^k \alpha_i^2 \int_\Omega v_i^2\,dx + o(r^2)\\ &= \frac{1}{2}\sum_{i=1}^k \left(1 - \frac{\lambda}{\lambda_i}\right)\alpha_i^2 + o(r^2) \end{aligned}$$

for small r. Since $\lambda > \lambda_k$, $I(u) < 0$ and the proof is complete.

As a second application of Theorem 9.6, we examine again the problem treated in (2.33) and Theorem 2.32:

$$-\Delta u = \lambda p(u), \qquad x \in \Omega, \qquad u = 0, \qquad x \in \partial\Omega. \tag{9.9}$$

THEOREM 9.10. *Suppose p satisfies* (p_1'), (p_3), (p_5), *and* (p_9). *Then for any* $j \in \mathbf{N}$, *there exists a* $\overline{\lambda}_j > 0$ *such that if* $\lambda > \overline{\lambda}_j$, (9.10) *possesses at least* j *distinct pairs of solutions.*

PROOF. As in the proof of Theorem 2.32, it suffices to show that the modified functional

$$I_\lambda(u) = \int_\Omega [\tfrac{1}{2}|\nabla u|^2 - \lambda\overline{P}(u)]\, dx \tag{9.11}$$

has the appropriate number of critical points. This in turn will follow from Theorem 9.1. In the proof of Theorem 2.32, it was already established that $I_\lambda \in C^1(E, \mathbf{R})$, is bounded from below, satisfies (PS), and $I_\lambda(0) = 0$. Clearly (p_9) implies I_λ is even. Thus we need only verify that for any $j \in \mathbf{N}$, there is a $\overline{\lambda}_j > 0$ such that for each $\lambda > \overline{\lambda}_j$, there is a set K as in Theorem 9.1. Let K be as in (9.8). For sufficiently small r, $\overline{P}(u(x)) = P(u(x))$ for all $u \in K$ and by (p_5), $P(u(x)) > 0$ if $u(x) \neq 0$. Therefore

$$\inf_{u\in K} \int_\Omega P(u(x))\, dx \equiv \alpha > 0.$$

Choose $\overline{\lambda} = \alpha^{-1}r^2$. Then $I_\lambda|_K \leq -\frac{1}{2}r^2 + o(r^2) < 0$ for small r. The proof is complete.

Now we turn to a $\mathbf{Z}_2$ version of the Mountain Pass Theorem. Such a result was stated in Chapter 1. A more general version will be given here.

THEOREM 9.12. *Let E be an infinite dimensional Banach space and let* $I \in C^1(E, \mathbf{R})$ *be even, satisfy (PS), and* $I(0) = 0$. *If* $E = V \oplus X$, *where V is finite dimensional, and I satisfies*

(I_1') *there are constants* $\rho, \alpha > 0$ *such that* $I|_{\partial B_\rho \cap X} \geq \alpha$, *and*

(I_2') *for each finite dimensional subspace* $\tilde{E} \subset E$, *there is an* $R = R(\tilde{E})$ *such that* $I \leq 0$ *on* $\tilde{E} \setminus B_{R(\tilde{E})}$,

then I possesses an unbounded sequence of critical values.

REMARK 9.13. All of our previous symmetric results have used roughly the same class of sets: $\gamma_k = \{A \in \mathcal{E} \,|\, \gamma(A) \geq k\}$ (or the corresponding class on ∂B_r) to construct critical values. These sets do not suffice for the setting of Theorem 9.13. To see why, as a model case consider a functional of the form

$$I(u) = \int_\Omega \left(\frac{1}{2}|\nabla u|^2 - \frac{1}{s+1}|u|^{s+1}\right) dx, \tag{9.14}$$

where $1 < s < (n+2)(n-2)^{-1}$. It will be seen later in this chapter that Theorem 9.12 applies to such a functional. Since $A \in \gamma_k$ can be chosen to be an arbitrarily large sphere in $\text{span}\{v_1, \ldots, v_k\}$ with v_i as in (2.40), (9.14) shows

$$\inf_{A \in \gamma_k} \sup_{u \in A} I(u) = -\infty. \tag{9.15}$$

On the other hand choosing

$$A = \text{span}\{v_j, \ldots, v_{j+k}\} \cap \partial B_r,$$

where $j = j(r)$ is large enough, and using arguments as in Corollary 8.18 we see $\min_{u \in A} I(u) \geq \frac{1}{4} r^2$. Hence

$$\sup_{A \in \gamma_k} \min_{u \in A} I(u) = \infty.$$

Thus a new family of sets must be produced to prove Theorem 9.12.

PROOF OF THEOREM 9.12. A sequence of families of sets Γ_m will be introduced and a corresponding sequence (c_m) of critical values of I will be obtained by taking a minimax of I over each Γ_m. A separate argument then shows (c_m) is unbounded.

Suppose V is k dimensional and $V = \text{span}\{e_1, \ldots, e_k\}$. For $m \geq k$, inductively choose $e_{m+1} \notin \text{span}\{e_1, \ldots, e_m\} \equiv E_m$. Set $R_m \equiv R(E_m)$ and $D_m \equiv B_{R_m} \cap E_m$. Let

$$G_m \equiv \{h \in C(D_m, E) | h \text{ is odd and } h = \text{id on } \partial B_{R_m} \cap E_m\}. \tag{9.16}$$

Note that $\text{id} \in G_m$ for all $m \in \mathbf{N}$ so $G_m \neq \emptyset$. Set

$$\Gamma_j \equiv \{h(\overline{D_m \setminus Y}) | h \in G_m, m \geq j, Y \in \mathcal{E}, \text{and } \gamma(Y) \leq m - j\}. \tag{9.17}$$

The following proposition shows that the sets Γ_j satisfy conditions like (8.3).

PROPOSITION 9.18. *The sets Γ_j possess the following properties:*

$1°$ $\Gamma_j \neq \emptyset$ *for all* $j \in \mathbf{N}$.

$2°$ (*Monotonicity*) $\Gamma_{j+1} \subset \Gamma_j$.

$3°$ (*Invariance*) *If* $\varphi \in C(E, E)$ *is odd, and* $\varphi = \text{id}$ *on* $\partial B_{R_m} \cap E_m$ *for all* $m \geq j$, *then* $\varphi \colon \Gamma_j \to \Gamma_j$.

$4°$ (*Excision*) *If* $B \in \Gamma_j$, $Z \in \mathcal{E}$, *and* $\gamma(Z) \leq s < j$, *then* $\overline{B \setminus Z} \in \Gamma_{j-s}$.

PROOF. Since $\text{id} \in G_m$ for all $m \in \mathbf{N}$, it follows that $\Gamma_j \notin \emptyset$ for all $j \in \mathbf{N}$. If $B = h(\overline{D_m \setminus Y}) \in \Gamma_{j+1}$, then $m \geq j+1 \geq j$, $h \in G_m$, $Y \in \mathcal{E}$, and $\gamma(Y) \leq m - (j+1) \leq m - j$. Therefore $B \in \Gamma_j$. Next to prove $3°$, suppose $B = h(\overline{D_m \setminus Y}) \in \Gamma_j$ and φ is as above. Then $\varphi \circ h$ is odd, belongs to $C(D_m, E)$, and $\varphi \circ h = \text{id}$ on $\partial B_{R_m} \cap E_m$. Therefore $\varphi \circ h \in G_m$ and $\varphi \circ h(\overline{D_m \setminus Y}) = \varphi(B) \in \Gamma_j$. Lastly to get $4°$, again let $B = h(\overline{D_m \setminus Y}) \in \Gamma_j$ and $Z \in \mathcal{E}$ with $\gamma(Z) \leq s < j$. We claim

$$\overline{B \setminus Z} = h(\overline{D_m \setminus (Y \cup h^{-1}(Z))}). \tag{9.19}$$

Assuming (9.19), note that since h is odd and continuous and $Z \in \mathcal{E}$, $h^{-1}(Z) \in \mathcal{E}$. Therefore $Y \cup h^{-1}(Z) \in \mathcal{E}$ and by 4° and 2° of Proposition 7.5,

$$\gamma(Y \cup h^{-1}(Z)) \le \gamma(Y) + \gamma(h^{-1}(Z)) \le \gamma(Y) + \gamma(Z)$$
$$\le m - j + s = m - (j - s).$$

Hence $\overline{B \setminus Z} \in \Gamma_{j-s}$.

To prove (9.19), suppose $b \in h(D_m \setminus (Y \cup h^{-1}(Z)))$. Then $b \in h(D_m \setminus Y) \setminus Z \subset B \setminus Z \subset \overline{B \setminus Z}$. Therefore

$$h(D_m \setminus (Y \cup h^{-1}(Z))) \subset \overline{B \setminus Z}. \tag{9.20}$$

On the other hand if $b \in B \setminus Z$, then $b = h(w)$ where

$$w \in \overline{D_m \setminus Y} \setminus h^{-1}(Z) \subset \overline{D_m \setminus (Y \cup h^{-1}(Z))}.$$

Thus

$$B \setminus Z \subset h(\overline{D_m \setminus (Y \cup h^{-1}(Z))}). \tag{9.21}$$

Comparing (9.20)–(9.21) yields (9.19) since h is continuous.

Now a sequence of minimax values of I can be defined. Set

$$c_j = \inf_{B \in \Gamma_j} \max_{u \in B} I(u), \qquad j \in \mathbf{N}. \tag{9.22}$$

It will soon be seen that if $j > k = \dim V$, c_j is a critical value of I. The following intersection theorem is needed to provide a key estimate.

PROPOSITION 9.23. *If $j > k$ and $B \in \Gamma_j$, then*

$$B \cap \partial B_\rho \cap X \ne \varnothing. \tag{9.24}$$

PROOF. Set $B = h(\overline{D_m \setminus Y})$ where $m \ge j$ and $\gamma(Y) \le m - j$. Let $\hat{\mathcal{O}} = \{x \in D_m | h(x) \in B_\rho\}$. Since h is odd, $0 \in \hat{\mathcal{O}}$. Let $\mathcal{O}$ denote the component of $\hat{\mathcal{O}}$ containing 0. Since D_m is bounded, $\mathcal{O}$ is a symmetric (with respect to 0) bounded neighborhood of 0 in E_m. Therefore by Proposition 7.7, $\gamma(\partial\mathcal{O}) = m$. We claim

$$h(\partial\mathcal{O}) \subset \partial B_\rho. \tag{9.25}$$

Assuming (9.25) for the moment, set $W \equiv \{x \in D_m | h(x) \in \partial B_\rho\}$. Therefore (9.25) implies $W \supset \partial\mathcal{O}$. Hence by 3° of Proposition 7.5, $\gamma(W) = m$ and by Remark 7.6, $\gamma(\overline{W \setminus Y}) \ge m - (m - j) = j > k$. Thus by 2° of Proposition 7.5, $\gamma(h(\overline{W \setminus Y})) > k$. Since $\operatorname{codim} X = k$, $h(\overline{W \setminus Y}) \cap X \ne \varnothing$ by Proposition 7.8. But $h(\overline{W \setminus Y}) \subset (B \cap \partial B_\rho)$. Consequently (9.24) holds.

It remains to prove (9.25). Note first that by the choice of R_m,

$$I \le 0 \quad \text{on } E_m \setminus B_{R_m}. \tag{9.26}$$

Since $m > k$, $\partial B_\rho \cap X \cap E_m \ne \varnothing$. Hence by (I_1'),

$$I|_{\partial B_\rho \cap X \cap E_m} \ge \alpha > 0. \tag{9.27}$$

Comparing (9.26) and (9.27) shows $R_m > \rho$. Now to verify (9.25), suppose $x \in \partial\mathcal{O}$ and $h(x) \in B_\rho$. If $x \in D_m$ there is a neighborhood N of x such that $h(N) \subset B_\rho$. But then $x \notin \partial\mathcal{O}$. Thus $x \in \partial D_m$ (with ∂ relative to E_m). But on ∂D_m, $h = \mathrm{id}$. Consequently if $x \in \partial D_m$ and $h(x) \in B_\rho$, $\|h(x)\| = \|x\| = R_m < \rho$ contrary to what we just proved. Thus (9.25) must hold.

REMARK 9.28. A closer inspection of the above proof shows that

$$\gamma(B \cap \partial B_\rho \cap X) \geq j - k.$$

COROLLARY 9.29. *If $j > k$, $c_j \geq \alpha > 0$.*

PROOF. If $j > k$ and $B \in \Gamma_j$, by (9.24) and (I_1'), $\max_{u \in B} I(u) \geq \alpha$. Therefore by (9.22), $c_j \geq \alpha$.

The next proposition both shows c_j is a critical value of I for $j > k$ and makes an appropriate multipicity statement about degenerate critical values.

PROPOSITION 9.30. *If $j > k$, and $c_j = \cdots = c_{j+p} \equiv c$, then $\gamma(K_c) \geq p+1$.*

PROOF. Since $I(0) = 0$ while $c \geq \alpha > 0$ via Corollary 9.29, $0 \notin K_c$. Therefore $K_c \in \mathcal{E}$ and by (PS), K_c is compact. If $\gamma(K_c) \leq p$, by 5° of Proposition 7.5, there is a $\delta > 0$ such that $\gamma(N_\delta(K_c)) \leq p$. Invoking the Deformation Theorem with $\mathcal{O} = N_\delta(K_c)$ and $\bar{\varepsilon} = \alpha/2$, there is an $\varepsilon \in (0, \bar{\varepsilon})$ and $\eta \in C([0,1] \times E, E)$ such that $\eta(1, \cdot)$ is odd and

$$\gamma(1, A_{c+\varepsilon} \setminus \mathcal{O}) \subset A_{c-\varepsilon}. \tag{9.31}$$

Choose $B \in \Gamma_{j+p}$ such that

$$\max_{u \in B} I(u) \leq c + \varepsilon. \tag{9.32}$$

By 4° of Proposition 9.18, $\overline{B \setminus \mathcal{O}} \in \Gamma_j$. The definition of R_m shows $I(u) \leq 0$ for $u \in \partial B_{R_m} \cap E_m$ for any $m \in \mathbf{N}$. Hence 2° of Theorem A.4 and our choice of $\bar{\varepsilon}$ imply $\eta(1, \cdot) = \mathrm{id}$ on $\partial B_{R_m} \cap E_m$ for each $m \in \mathbf{N}$. Consequently $\eta(1, \overline{B \setminus \mathcal{O}}) \in \Gamma_j$ by 3° of Proposition 9.18. The definition of c_j and (9.31)–(9.32) then imply

$$\max_{\eta(1, \overline{B \setminus \mathcal{O}})} I \leq c - \varepsilon,$$

a contradiction,.

The next proposition completes the proof of Theorem 9.12.

PROPOSITION 9.33. *$c_j \to \infty$ as $j \to \infty$.*

PROOF. By 2° of Proposition 9.18 and (9.22), $c_{j+1} \geq c_j$. Suppose the sequence (c_j) is bounded. Then $c_j \to \bar{c} < \infty$ as $j \to \infty$. If $c_j = \bar{c}$ for all large j, Proposition 9.30 implies $\gamma(K_{\bar{c}}) = \infty$. But by (PS), $K_{\bar{c}}$ is compact so $\gamma(K_{\bar{c}}) < \infty$ via 5° of Proposition 7.5. Thus $\bar{c} > c_j$ for all $j \in \mathbf{N}$. Set

$$\mathcal{K} \equiv \{u \in E | c_{k+1} \leq I(u) \leq \bar{c} \text{ and } I'(u) = 0\}.$$

By (PS) again, $\mathcal{K}$ is compact and 5° of Proposition 7.5 implies $\gamma(\mathcal{K}) < \infty$ and there is a $\delta > 0$ such that $\gamma(N_\delta(\mathcal{K})) = \gamma(\mathcal{K}) \equiv q$. Let $s = \max(q, k+1)$. The

Deformation Theorem with $c = \overline{c}$, $\overline{\varepsilon} = \overline{c} - c_s$, and $\mathcal{O} = N_\delta(\mathcal{K})$ yields an ε and η as usual such that

$$\eta(1, A_{\overline{c}+\varepsilon} \setminus \mathcal{O}) \subset A_{\overline{c}-\varepsilon}. \tag{9.34}$$

Choose $j \in \mathbf{N}$ such that $c_j > \overline{c} - \varepsilon$ and $B \in \Gamma_{j+s}$ such that

$$\max_B I \le \overline{c} + \varepsilon. \tag{9.35}$$

Arguing as in the proof of Proposition 9.30 shows $\overline{B \setminus \mathcal{O}}$ is in Γ_j as is $\eta(1, \overline{B \setminus \mathcal{O}})$ provided that $\eta(1, \cdot) = \mathrm{id}$ on $\partial B_{R_m} \cap E_m$ for all $m \ge j$. But $I \le 0$ on $\partial B_{R_m} \cap E_m$ for all $m \in \mathbf{N}$ while $\overline{c} - \overline{\varepsilon} = c_s \ge c_{k+1} \ge \alpha > 0$ via Corollary 9.29. Consequently $\eta(1, \overline{B \setminus \mathcal{O}}) \in \Gamma_j$ and by (9.34)–(9.35) and the choice of c_j,

$$c_j \le \max_{\eta(1, \overline{B \setminus \mathcal{O}})} I \le \overline{c} - \varepsilon < c_j,$$

a contradiction. The proof is complete.

REMARKS 9.36. (i) If E is finite dimensional, the result of Theorem 9.12 also obtains with the conclusion being that I possesses at least $\dim X$ critical points.

(ii) There are analogues of Theorem 9.12 when V is infinite dimensional and when we have an S^1 rather than a $\mathbf{Z}_2$ action (see e.g. [**FHR**]). Such a result leads to the generalization of Theorem 6.10 mentioned in Remark 6.45.

As an application of Theorem 9.12, consider

$$\begin{aligned} -\Delta u &= p(x, u), \qquad x \in \Omega, \\ u &= 0, \qquad x \in \partial\Omega. \end{aligned} \tag{9.37}$$

THEOREM 9.38. *Suppose p satisfies $(p_1), (p_2), (p_4)$, and (p_9). Then* (9.37) *possesses an unbounded sequence of weak solutions.*

PROOF. With $E = W_0^{1,2}(\Omega)$ as usual and

$$I(u) = \int_\Omega [\tfrac{1}{2}|\nabla u|^2 - P(x, u)]\, dx,$$

the proof of Theorem 2.15 shows $I \in C^1(E, \mathbf{R})$, satisfies (PS), and $I(0) = 0$. Moreover the argument in Theorem 2.15 that showed I satisfied (I_2) equally well yields (I_2'). Clearly (p_9) implies I is even. Assume for now that I also satisfies (I_1'). Then Theorem 9.12 implies that I possesses an unbounded sequence of critical values $c_k = I(u_k)$, where u_k is a weak solution of (9.37). Since $I'(u_k)u_k = 0$,

$$\int_\Omega |\nabla u_k|^2\, dx = \int_\Omega p(x, u_k) u_k\, dx \tag{9.39}$$

and it follows that

$$c_k = \int_\Omega [\tfrac{1}{2} p(x, u_k) u_k - P(x, u_k)]\, dx \to \infty \tag{9.40}$$

as $k \to \infty$. Hence by (9.39)–(9.40) and (p_4), (u_k) must be unbounded in E and in $L^\infty(\Omega)$.

To verify (I_1'), choose $V = \text{span}\{v_1, \dots, v_k\}$ where the functions v_j are as in (2.40) and $X = V^\perp$. By (p_2), for all $u \in E$,

$$I(u) \geq \int_\Omega \tfrac{1}{2}|\nabla u|^2\, dx - a_5 \int_\Omega |u|^{s+1}\, dx - a_6. \tag{9.41}$$

By (8.21)–(8.22), if $u \in \partial B_\rho \cap X$,

$$I(u) \geq \rho^2 \left(\tfrac{1}{2} - a_7 \lambda_{k+1}^{-(1-a)(s+1)/2} \rho^{s-1}\right) - a_8. \tag{9.42}$$

Choose $\rho = \rho(k)$ so that the coefficient of ρ^2 in (9.42) is $\frac{1}{4}$. Therefore

$$I(u) \geq \tfrac{1}{4}\rho^2 - a_8 \tag{9.43}$$

for $u \in \partial B_\rho \cap X$. Since $\lambda_k \to \infty$ as $k \to \infty$, $\rho(k) \to \infty$ as $k \to \infty$. Choose k so that $\frac{1}{4}\rho^2 > 2a_8$. Consequently

$$I(u) \geq \tfrac{1}{8}\rho^2 \equiv \alpha \tag{9.44}$$

and (I_1') holds.

As a final example of the ideas used in the proof of Theorem 9.12, consider (9.9) again. In Theorem 9.10, we proved under appropriate hypotheses on p if $\lambda > \overline{\lambda}_k$, (9.9) possesses at least k distinct pairs of weak solutions and these functions correspond to negative critical values of (9.11). Let K be as in (9.8), i.e. $K = \partial B_r \cap E_k$. By our choice of r and $\overline{\lambda}_k$, $I < 0$ on K. Setting $R_m = r$ and $D_m = B_r \cap E_m$, define G_m for $1 \leq m \leq k$ as in (9.16) and define Γ_j as in (9.17) with the further proviso that $m \leq k$. Proposition 9.18 then holds for $j \in [1, k]$ and $m \leq k$ as does Proposition 9.23. Defining c_j via (9.22), observing that $\eta(1, \cdot) = \text{id}$ on $\partial B_r \cap E_k$, and noting that Corollary 9.29 holds with $k = 0$, the proof of Proposition 9.30 works equally well in this setting. Thus we have proved:

THEOREM 9.45 [**AR**]. *Under the hypotheses of Theorem 9.10, for all $\lambda > \overline{\lambda}_k$, (9.9) possesses at least $2k$ distinct pairs of nontrivial solutions, k pairs corresponding to negative and k pairs to positive critical values of (9.11).*

10. Perturbations from Symmetry

In the last two chapters several examples have been given of the existence of multiple critical points for functionals invariant under a group of symmetries. A natural question to ask is: What happens when such a functional is subjected to a perturbation which destroys the symmetry? Some special cases of this question have been studied and while progress has been made, there are not yet satisfactory general answers.

This chapters treats a perturbation question in the setting of Theorem 9.38. Thus consider

$$(10.1)\qquad \begin{aligned} -\Delta u &= p(x,u), \qquad x\in\Omega,\\ u &= 0, \qquad x\in\partial\Omega, \end{aligned}$$

where p satisfies $(p_1), (p_2), (p_4)$, and (p_9). By Theorem 9.38 the corresponding functional has an unbounded sequence of critical values and (10.1) has an unbounded sequence of weak solutions. Suppose $f\in L^2(\Omega)$ and (10.1) is replaced by

$$(10.2)\qquad \begin{aligned} -\Delta u &= p(x,u)+f(x), \qquad x\in\Omega,\\ u &= 0, \qquad x\in\partial\Omega. \end{aligned}$$

The corresponding functional is

$$(10.3)\qquad I(u)=\int_\Omega [\tfrac{1}{2}|\nabla u|^2 - P(x,u) - f(x)u]\,dx$$

and I is not even if $f\not\equiv 0$. Nevertheless we have:

THEOREM 10.4 [**R8**]. *If p satisfies $(p_1), (p_2), (p_4)$, and (p_9) and $f\in L^2(\Omega)$, then (10.2) possesses an unbounded sequence of weak solutions provided that s in (p_2) is further restricted by*

$$(10.5)\qquad \beta\equiv\frac{(n+2)-(n-2)s}{n(s-1)} > \frac{\mu}{\mu-1}.$$

REMARKS 10.6. (i) Inequality (10.5) is equivalent to

$$(10.7)\qquad s<\frac{\mu n+(\mu-1)(n+2)}{\mu n+(\mu-1)(n-2)}.$$

It is easily checked that if s satisfies (10.7), then $s<(n+2)(n-2)^{-1}$. Also, observing that $s=1$ and $\mu=2$ satisfies (10.7) shows that (10.5) is nonvacuous.

(ii) Slightly less general versions of Theorem 10.4 were proved by Bahri and Berestycki [**BB**] and by Struwe [**S1**]. See also Dong and Li [**DL**]. Their arguments differ from the one given here, which is somewhat in the spirit of the symmetric Mountain Pass Theorem. For the proof we require an estimate on the deviation from symmetry of I of the form

$$|I(u) - I(-u)| \leq \beta_1(|I(u)|^{1/\mu} + 1) \tag{10.8}$$

for $u \in E$. Unfortunately I does not satisty (10.8); however it can be modified in such a fashion that the new functional, J, satisfies (10.8) and large critical values and points of J are critical values and points of I.

To motivate the modified problem, a priori bounds for critical points of I in terms of the corresponding critical values will be obtained. Note first that by (p_4) there are constants $a_4, a_5 > 0$ such that

$$P(x, \xi) \geq a_5|\xi|^\mu - a_4 \tag{10.9}$$

for all $\xi \in \mathbf{R}$. Therefore there is a constant $a_3 > 0$ such that

$$\frac{1}{\mu}(\xi p(x, \xi) + a_3) \geq P(x, \xi) + a_4 \geq a_5|\xi|^\mu \tag{10.10}$$

for all $\xi \in \mathbf{R}$.

PROPOSITION 10.11. *Under the hypotheses of Theorem* 10.4, *there exists a constant A depending on $\|f\|_{L^2(\Omega)}$ such that if u is a critical point of I,*

$$\int_\Omega (P(x, u) + a_4)\, dx \leq A(I(u)^2 + 1)^{1/2}. \tag{10.12}$$

REMARK 10.13. If u is a critical point of (10.3), then (10.10) and (10.12) easily imply a bound for u in E in terms of $I(u)$.

PROOF OF PROPOSITION 10.11. Suppose u is a critical point of I. Then by (10.10) and simple estimates,

$$\begin{aligned} I(u) = I(u) - \frac{1}{2}I'(u)u &= \int_\Omega \left[\frac{1}{2}up(x, u) - P(x, u) - \frac{1}{2}fu\right] dx \\ &\geq \left(\frac{1}{2} - \frac{1}{\mu}\right) \int_\Omega (up(x, u) + a_3)\, dx - \frac{1}{2}\|f\|_{L^2(\Omega)}\|u\|_{L^2(\Omega)} - a_6 \\ &\geq a_7 \int_\Omega (P(x, u) + a_4)\, dx - a_8\|u\|_{L^\mu(\Omega)} - a_6 \\ &\geq \frac{a_7}{2} \int_\Omega (P(x, u) + a_4)\, dx - a_9 \end{aligned} \tag{10.14}$$

and (10.12) follows immediately from (10.14).

To introduce the modified problem, let $\chi \in C^\infty(\mathbf{R}, \mathbf{R})$ such that $\chi(\xi) \equiv 1$ for $\xi \leq 1$, $\chi(\xi) \equiv 0$ for $\xi \geq 2$, and $\chi'(\xi) \in (-2, 0)$ for $\xi \in (1, 2)$. Set

$$Q(u) \equiv 2A(I(u)^2 + 1)^{1/2}$$

and

$$\psi(u) \equiv \chi\left(Q(u)^{-1} \int_\Omega (P(x, u) + a_4)\, dx\right).$$

Note that by (10.12), if u is a critical point of I, the argument of χ lies in $[0, \frac{1}{2}]$ and therefore $\psi(u) = 1$. Finally set

$$J(u) \equiv \int_\Omega [\tfrac{1}{2}|\nabla u|^2 - P(x,u) - \psi(u) f u]\, dx. \tag{10.15}$$

Then $J(u) = I(u)$ if u is a critical point of I. The following result contains the main technical properties of J which we need.

PROPOSITION 10.16. *Under the hypotheses of Theorem* 10.4:

1° $J \in C^1(E, \mathbf{R})$.

2° *There exists a constant* β_1 *depending on* $\|f\|_{L^2(\Omega)}$ *such that*

$$|J(u) - J(-u)| \le \beta_1(|J(u)|^{1/\mu} + 1) \tag{10.17}$$

for all $u \in E$.

3° *There is a constant* $M_0 > 0$ *such that if* $J(u) \ge M_0$ *and* $J'(u) = 0$, *then* $J(u) = I(u)$ *and* $I'(u) = 0$.

4° *There is a constant* $M_1 \ge M_0$ *such that for any* $c > M_1$, J *satisfies* $(PS)_{\rm loc}$ *at* c.

PROOF. Hypotheses (p_1)–(p_2) imply $I \in C^1(E, \mathbf{R})$. Since χ is smooth, the same is true for ψ and therefore J. To prove 2°, note first that if $u \in \operatorname{supp} \psi$ (the support of ψ), then

$$\left| \int_\Omega f u\, dx \right| \le \alpha_1(|I(u)|^{1/\mu} + 1), \tag{10.18}$$

where α_1 depends on $\|f\|_{L^2(\Omega)}$. Indeed by the Schwarz and Hölder inequalities and (10.10),

$$\begin{aligned} \left| \int_\Omega f u\, dx \right| &\le \|f\|_{L^2(\Omega)} \|u\|_{L^2(\Omega)} \le \alpha_2 \|u\|_{L^\mu(\Omega)} \\ &\le \alpha_3 \left(\int_\Omega (P(x,u) + a_4)\, dx \right)^{1/\mu} \end{aligned} \tag{10.19}$$

If further $u \in \operatorname{supp} \psi$,

$$\int_\Omega (P(x,u) + a_4)\, dx \le 4A(I(u)^2 + 1)^{1/2} \le \alpha_4(|I(u)| + 1) \tag{10.20}$$

so (10.18) follows from (10.19)–(10.20). Now to get (10.17), by (10.15) and (p_9),

$$|J(u) - J(-u)| \le (\psi(u) + \psi(-u)) \left| \int_\Omega f u\, dx \right|. \tag{10.21}$$

To estimate the right-hand side of (10.21), by (10.18),

$$\psi(u) \left| \int_\Omega f u\, dx \right| \le \alpha_1 \psi(u)(|I(u)|^{1/\mu} + 1). \tag{10.22}$$

By (10.3) and (10.15),

$$|I(u)| \le |J(u)| + \left| \int_\Omega f u\, dx \right|. \tag{10.23}$$

Therefore

$$\psi(u)\left|\int_\Omega fu\,dx\right| \le \alpha_5\psi(u)\left(|J(u)|^{1/\mu} + \left|\int_\Omega fu\,dx\right|^{1/\mu} + 1\right). \tag{10.24}$$

Using Young's inequality, the f term on the right-hand side can be absorbed into the left-hand side yielding

$$\psi(u)\left|\int_\Omega fu\,dx\right| \le \alpha_6(|J(u)|^{1/\mu} + 1). \tag{10.25}$$

Combining (10.25) with a similar estimate for the $\psi(-u)$ term gives (10.17).

To prove 3°, it suffices to show that if M_0 is large and u is a critical point of J with $J(u) \ge M_0$, then

$$Q(u)^{-1}\int_\Omega (P(x,u) + a_4)\,dx < 1. \tag{10.26}$$

The definition of ψ then implies $\psi(v) \equiv 1$ for v near u. Hence $\psi'(u) = 0$ so $J(u) = I(u)$, $J'(u) = I'(u)$, and 3° follows.

We will show that (10.26) holds. By the definition of J,

$$J'(u)u = \int_\Omega [|\nabla u|^2 - up(x,u) - (\psi(u) + \psi'(u)u)fu]\,dx, \tag{10.27}$$

where

$$\psi'(u)u = \chi'(\theta(u))Q(u)^{-2}\left[Q(u)\int_\Omega up(x,u)\,dx - (2A)^2\theta(u)I(u)I'(u)u\right] \tag{10.28}$$

and

$$\theta(u) = Q^{-1}(u)\int_\Omega (P(x,u) + a_4)\,dx.$$

Regrouping terms in (10.27)–(10.28) yields

$$\begin{aligned} J'(u)u &= (1 + T_1(u))\int_\Omega |\nabla u|^2\,dx \\ &\quad - (1 + T_2(u))\int_\Omega up(x,u)\,dx - (\psi(u) + T_1(u))\int_\Omega fu\,dx, \end{aligned} \tag{10.29}$$

where

$$T_1(u) \equiv \chi'(\theta(u))(2A)^2Q(u)^{-2}I(u)\int_\Omega fu\,dx \tag{10.30)(i}$$

and

$$T_2(u) \equiv \chi'(\theta(u))Q(u)^{-1}\int_\Omega fu\,dx + T_1(u). \tag{10.30)(ii}$$

Consider

$$J(u) - \frac{1}{2(1 + T_1(u))}J'(u)u. \tag{10.31}$$

If $\psi(u) = 1$ and $T_1(u) = 0 = T_2(u)$, (10.31) reduces to the left-hand side of (10.14) so (10.26) follows from (10.12). Since $0 \le \psi(u) \le 1$, if $T_1(u)$ and $T_2(u)$

are both small enough, the calculation made in (10.14) when carried out for (10.31) leads to (10.12) with A replaced by a larger constant which is smaller than $2A$. But then (10.26) holds.

It therefore suffices to show that $T_1(u), T_2(u) \to 0$ as $M_0 \to \infty$. If $u \notin \operatorname{supp} \psi$, $T_1(u) = 0 = T_2(u)$. Thus we assume $u \in \operatorname{supp} \psi$. By (10.30) and (10.18),

$$|T_1(u)| \le 4\alpha_1(|I(u)|^{1/\mu} + 1)|I(u)|^{-1}. \tag{10.32}$$

We need an estimate relating $I(u)$ and $J(u)$ for $u \in \operatorname{supp} \psi$. By (10.3) and (10.15),

$$I(u) \ge J(u) - \left| \int_\Omega fu\, dx \right|.$$

Thus by (10.18),

$$I(u) + \alpha_1 |I(u)|^{1/\mu} \ge J(u) - \alpha_1 \ge M_0/2 \tag{10.33}$$

for M_0 large enough. If $I(u) \le 0$, (10.33) implies

$$\alpha_1^\nu/\nu + |I(u)|/\mu \ge M_0/2 + |I(u)|, \tag{10.34}$$

where $\nu^{-1} + \mu^{-1} = 1$. But (10.34) is not possible if M_0 is large enough, e.g., $M_0 \ge 2\alpha_1^\nu \nu^{-1}$, which we can assume to be the case. Therefore $I(u) > 0$. Hence (10.33) implies $I(u) \ge M_0/4$ or $I(u) \ge (M_0/4\alpha_1)^\mu$. In any event, $I(u) \to \infty$ as $M_0 \to \infty$, which together with (10.32) shows $T_1(u) \to 0$ as $M_0 \to \infty$. Analogous estimates yield $T_2(u) \to 0$ as $M_0 \to \infty$ and 3° holds.

The verification of 4° follows similar lines to 3°. It suffices to show there is an $M_1 > M_0$ such that if $(u_m) \subset E$, $M_1 \le J(u_m) \le K$, and $J'(u_m) \to 0$, then (u_m) is bounded. For large m and any $\rho > 0$,

$$\begin{aligned} \rho\|u_m\| + K &\ge J(u_m) - \rho J'(u_m)u_m \\ &= (\tfrac{1}{2} - \rho(1 + T_1(u_m)))\|u_m\|^2 \\ &\quad + \rho(1 + T_2(u_m)) \int_\Omega u_m p(x, u_m)\, dx - \int_\Omega P(x, u_m)\, dx \\ &\quad + [\rho(\psi(u_m) + T_1(u_m)) - \psi(u_m)] \int_\Omega f u_m\, dx. \end{aligned} \tag{10.35}$$

For M_1 sufficiently large and therefore T_1, T_2 small, we can choose $\rho \in (\mu^{-1}, 2^{-1})$ and $\varepsilon > 0$ such that

$$\frac{1}{2(1 + T_1(u_m))} > \rho + \varepsilon > \rho - \varepsilon > \frac{1}{\mu(1 + T_2(u_m))}. \tag{10.36}$$

Hence by (10.35), (10.36), and (p_4),

$$\rho\|u_m\| + K \ge \frac{\varepsilon}{2}\|u_m\|^2 + \frac{\varepsilon}{2}\mu a_5 \|u_m\|^\mu_{L^\mu(\Omega)} - \alpha_2 - \alpha_3 \|u_m\|^2_{L^2(\Omega)}. \tag{10.37}$$

Using the Hölder and Young inequalities, (10.37) implies (u_m) is bounded in E. As in Proposition B.35,

$$D^{-1}J'(u_m) = (1 + T_1(u_m))u_m - \mathcal{P}(u_m),$$

where $D\colon E \to E^*$ is the duality map, P is compact, and $|T_1(u_m)| \le \frac{1}{2}$ (for M_1 large). Hence (PS) holds.

On the basis of 3° of Proposition 10.16 and the argument of Theorem 9.38, to prove Theorem 10.4 it suffices to show that J has an unbounded sequence of critical points. This we shall do via a series of steps. The first is to introduce a sequence of minimax values of J. Let the functions (v_j) be as in (2.40) (with e.g. $a(x) \equiv 1$), let $E_j \equiv \operatorname{span}\{v_1, \dots, v_j\}$, and let $E_j^\perp$ be the orthogonal complement of E_j in E. Comparing J to the functional in Theorem 9.38, the ψ term in J does not affect the verification of (I_2') for J. Therefore there is an $R_j > 0$ such that $J(u) \le 0$ if $u \in E_j \setminus B_{R_j}$. Set $D_j \equiv B_{R_j} \cap E_j$ and

$$G_j \equiv \{h \in C(D_j, E) | h \text{ is odd and } h = \text{id on } \partial B_{R_j} \cap E_j\}.$$

Define

$$b_j \equiv \inf_{h \in G_j} \max_{u \in D_j} J(h(u)), \qquad j \in \mathbf{N}. \tag{10.38}$$

These minimax values will not in general be critical values of J unless $f \equiv 0$. However we will use them as part of a comparison argument to prove that J has an unbounded sequence of critical values. First we will obtain lower bounds for b_j.

PROPOSITION 10.39. *There is a constant $\beta_2 > 0$ and $\tilde{k} \in \mathbf{N}$ such that for all $k \ge \tilde{k}$,*

$$b_k \ge \beta_2 k^\beta, \tag{10.40}$$

where β was defined in (10.5).

PROOF. Let $h \in G_k$ and $\rho < R_k$. By Proposition 9.23, there exists a $w \in h(D_k) \cap \partial B_\rho \cap E_{k-1}^\perp$. Therefore

$$\max_{u \in D_k} J(h(u)) \ge J(w) \ge \inf_{u \in \partial B_\rho \cap E_{k-1}^\perp} J(u). \tag{10.41}$$

To obtain a lower bound for the right-hand side of (10.41), we argue along the same lines as (9.41)–(9.44) of Theorem 9.38 to choose $\rho = \rho_k$ satisfying

$$\rho_k^{s-1} = \text{const}\, \lambda_k^{(1-a)(s+1)2^{-1}},$$

and therefore

$$J(u) \ge \tfrac{1}{4}\rho_k^2 - a_5 \tag{10.42}$$

for all $u \in \partial B_{\rho_k} \cap E_{k-1}^\perp$. Since $\lambda_k \ge a_6 k^{2/n}$ for large k [**CH**], (10.42) and our choice of ρ_k yield (10.40) for large k.

To get critical values of J from the sequence (b_k), another set of minimax values must be introduced. Define

$$U_k \equiv \{u \equiv tv_{k+1} + w | t \in [0, R_{k+1}], w \in B_{R_{k+1}} \cap E_k, \|u\| \le R_{k+1}\}$$

and
$$\Lambda_k = \{H \in C(U_k, E) | H|_{D_k} \in \Gamma_k \text{ and } H = \text{id for}$$
$$u \in Q_k \equiv (\partial B_{R_{k+1}} \cap E_{k+1}) \cup [(B_{R_{k+1}} \setminus B_{R_k}) \cap E_k]\}.$$

Set
$$c_k = \inf_{H \in \Lambda_k} \max_{u \in U_k} J(H(u)).$$

Comparing the definition of c_k to (10.38) shows $c_k \geq b_k$.

PROPOSITION 10.43. *Assume $c_k > b_k \geq M_1$. For $\delta \in (0, c_k - b_k)$, define*
$$\Lambda_k(\delta) \equiv \{H \in \Lambda_k | J(H(u)) \leq b_k + \delta \text{ for } u \in D_k\}$$

and

$$c_k(\delta) \equiv \inf_{H \in \Lambda_k(\delta)} \max_{u \in U_k} J(H(u)). \tag{10.44}$$

Then $c_k(\delta)$ is a critical value of J.

PROOF. The definition of $\Lambda_k(\delta)$ implies this set is nonempty. Since $\Lambda_k(\delta) \subset \Lambda_k$, $c_k(\delta) \geq c_k$. Suppose $c_k(\delta)$ is not a critical value of J. Set $\bar{\varepsilon} = \frac{1}{2}(c_k - b_k - \delta)$ so $\bar{\varepsilon} > 0$ and invoke the Deformation Theorem obtaining ε and η as usual. Choose $H \in \Lambda_k(\delta)$ such that

$$\max_{u \in U_k} J(H(u)) \leq c_k(\delta) + \varepsilon. \tag{10.45}$$

Consider $\eta(1, H(\cdot))$. Clearly this function belongs to $C(U_k, E)$. Moreover if $u \in Q_k$, $H(u) = u$ since $H \in \Lambda_k$ and therefore $J(H(u)) \leq 0$ via the definitions of R_k and R_{k+1}. Since we can assume $b_k \geq M_1 > 0$ and $c_k(\delta) \geq c_k > b_k$, the choice of $\bar{\varepsilon}$ implies $\eta(1, H(u)) = u$ on Q_k. Therefore $\eta(1, H(\cdot)) \in \Lambda_k$. Moreover since $H \in \Lambda_k(\delta)$, if $u \in D_k$,
$$J(H(u)) \leq b_k + \varepsilon \leq c_k - \bar{\varepsilon} \leq c_k(\delta) - \bar{\varepsilon}$$
by the choice of $\bar{\varepsilon}$. Therefore by 2° of Theorem A.4, $\eta(1, H(\cdot)) \in \Lambda_k(\delta)$. Consequently by (9.45) and 7° of Theorem A.4
$$\max_{u \in U_k} J(\eta(1, H(u))) \leq c_k(\delta) - \varepsilon,$$
contrary to (10.44).

Now we are nearly through with the proof of Theorem 10.4. If $c_k > b_k$ for a sequence of k's $\to \infty$, by Proposition 10.43 and 10.39, J has an unbounded sequence of critical values and the proof is complete. It remains to show that $c_k = b_k$ for all large k is impossible.

PROPOSITION 10.46. *If $c_k = b_k$ for all $k \geq k^*$, there exists a constant $\omega > 0$ and $\hat{k} \geq k^*$ such that*

$$b_k \leq \omega k^{\mu/(\mu-1)} \tag{10.47}$$

for all $k \geq \hat{k}$.

Comparing (10.47) to (10.40) and (10.5) yields a contradiction and the proof of Theorem 10.4 is complete.

PROOF OF PROPOSITION 10.46. Let $\varepsilon > 0$ and $k \geq k^*$. Choose $H \in \Lambda_k$ such that

$$\max_{u \in U_k} J(H(u)) \leq b_k + \varepsilon. \tag{10.48}$$

Since $D_{k+1} = U_k \cup (-U_k)$, H can be continuously extended to D_{k+1} as an odd function. Therefore by (10.38),

$$b_{k+1} \leq \max_{u \in D_{k+1}} J(H(u)) = J(H(w)) \tag{10.49}$$

for some $w \in D_{k+1}$. If $w \in U_k$, by (10.48)–(10.49),

$$J(H(w)) \leq b_k + \varepsilon. \tag{10.50}$$

Suppose $w \in -U_k$. Then since $b_k \to \infty$ as $k \to \infty$ via (10.40), (10.49) and (10.17) imply $J(-H(w)) > 0$ if k is large, e.g. $k \geq \hat{k}$. By (10.17), the oddness of H, and (10.48),

$$\begin{aligned} J(H(w)) = J(-H(-w)) &\leq J(H(-w)) + \beta_1 \left((J(H(-w)))^{1/\mu} + 1 \right) \\ &\leq b_k + \varepsilon + \beta_1((b_k + \varepsilon)^{1/\mu} + 1). \end{aligned} \tag{10.51}$$

Combining (10.49)–(10.51) yields

$$b_{k+1} \leq b_k + \varepsilon + \beta_1((b_k + \varepsilon)^{1/\mu} + 1). \tag{10.52}$$

Since ε is arbitrary, (10.52) implies

$$b_{k+1} \leq b_k + \beta_1(b_k^{1/\mu} + 1) \tag{10.53}$$

for all $k \geq \hat{k}$.

It remains to show that (10.53) implies (10.47). This will be done by induction. Suppose (10.47) holds for all $k \in [\hat{k}, j] \cap \mathbf{N}$. We claim it also holds for $j+1$. Without loss of generality, we can assume $j \geq 2\hat{k}$ and

$$\omega \geq \max_{0 \leq l \leq \hat{k}} \frac{b_{\hat{k}+l}}{(\hat{k}+l)^{\mu/\mu+1}}.$$

By (10.53),

$$\begin{aligned} b_{j+1} &\leq b_j + \beta_1((\omega j^{\mu/\mu-1})^{1/\mu} + 1) \\ &\leq b_{\hat{k}} + \beta_1 \sum_{l=\hat{k}}^{j} (\omega^{1/\mu} l^{1/\mu-1} + 1) \\ &\leq b_{\hat{k}} + \beta_1(j - \hat{k} + 1) + \beta_1 \omega^{1/\mu} \sum_{l=\hat{k}}^{j} l^{1/\mu-1}. \end{aligned} \tag{10.54}$$

We must prove that the right-hand side of (10.54) does not exceed $\omega(j+1)^{\mu/\mu-1}$. Now

$$\sum_{l=\hat{k}}^{j} l^{1/\mu-1} \leq \int_{\hat{k}}^{j} x^{1/\mu-1}\, dx \leq \frac{\mu-1}{\mu} j^{\mu/\mu-1}. \tag{10.55}$$

Comparing (10.54) and (10.55), we see that to get (10.47) for $j+1$, it suffices that ω satisfies

$$(10.56)\qquad \begin{aligned} &\text{(i)}\quad b_{\hat{k}} \le \omega(1-2\delta)(j+1)^{\mu/\mu-1},\\ &\text{(ii)}\quad \beta_1 \le \omega\delta,\\ &\text{(iii)}\quad \beta_1\omega^{1/\mu}\frac{\mu}{\mu-1} \le \omega\delta \end{aligned}$$

for some $\delta \in (0,1)$. Since $j \ge 2\hat{k}$, (10.56)(i) holds if

$$(10.57)\qquad 1 \le (1-2\delta)2^{\mu/\mu-1},$$

which is certainly satisfied for δ near 0. With δ so chosen, (10.57)(ii) and (iii) also hold if ω is large enough. Thus we have (10.47) for all $k \ge \hat{k}$ and the proof is complete.

REMARKS 10.58. (i) If $f(x)$ in (10.2) is replaced by $f(x,u)$, where

$$(10.59)\qquad |f(x,\xi)| \le \alpha_3 + \alpha_4|\xi|^\sigma, \qquad 0 \le \sigma < \mu - 1,$$

and (10.5) is strengthened to

$$(10.60)\qquad \frac{(n+2)-(n-2)s}{n(s-1)} > \frac{\mu}{\mu-(\sigma+1)},$$

a variant of our above arguments gives a stronger version of Theorem 10.4 for this case.

(ii) It is an interesting open question as to whether Theorem 10.4 holds without (10.5). Bahri [**Ba**] has given a partial answer. He proved for

$$\begin{aligned} -\Delta u &= |u|^{s-1}u + f(x), \qquad x \in \Omega,\\ u &= 0, \qquad x \in \partial\Omega, \end{aligned}$$

where $s < (n+2)(n-2)^{-1}$, that there is an open dense set of f in $W^{-1,2}(\Omega)$ for which (10.1) possesses an infinite number of distinct weak solutions.

(iii) A recent announcement of Bahri and P. L. Lions [**BL**] improves the value of s in (10.5) to $s < n(n-2)^{-1}$.

11. Variational Methods in Bifurcation Theory

In this final chapter, the use of variational methods in bifurcation theory will be studied. Recall that if X and Y are Banach spaces, $\mathcal{F}\colon X \to Y$, and $\mathcal{F}^{-1}(0)$ contains a curve $\mathcal{Z}$, we say an interior point $z \in \mathcal{Z}$ is a *bifurcation point for $\mathcal{F}$ with respect to $\mathcal{Z}$* if every neighborhood of z contains zeros of $\mathcal{F}$ not on $\mathcal{Z}$. After some preliminary transformations a situation often encountered in applications is $X = \mathbf{R} \times E$ with E a real Banach space, $Y = E$, and

$$\mathcal{F}(\lambda, u) = Lu + H(u) - \lambda u, \tag{11.1}$$

where $\lambda \in \mathbf{R}$, $u \in E$, $L \in \mathcal{L}(E, E)$, and $H \in C^1(E, E)$ with $H(u) = o(\|u\|)$ as $u \to 0$. Then we can take $\mathcal{Z} \equiv \{(\lambda, 0) | \lambda \in \mathbf{R}\}$ or any subinterval thereof. It is easy to verify that a necessary condition for $(\mu, 0) \in \mathcal{Z}$ to be a bifurcation point is that $\mu \in \sigma(L)$. Indeed if $\mu \notin \sigma(L)$, then for λ near μ, $L - \lambda \,\mathrm{id}$ is an isomorphism and $\mathcal{F}(\lambda, u) = 0$ is equivalent to

$$u = -(L - \lambda \,\mathrm{id})^{-1} H(u). \tag{11.2}$$

The right-hand side of (11.2) is $o(\|u\|)$ as $u \to 0$, while $u\|u\|^{-1}$ is of norm 1. Hence $\{(\lambda, 0) | \lambda$ is near $\mu\}$ are the only "small" solutions of (11.2) for λ near μ and $(\mu, 0)$ is not a bifurcation point.

Simple examples show this necessary condition is not sufficient. E.g. take $E = \mathbf{R}^2$, $u = (u_1, u_2)$, $L = \mathrm{id}$, and $H(u) = (-u_2^3, u_1^3)$ so $\mathcal{F}(\lambda, u) = 0$ becomes

$$\begin{pmatrix} 0 \\ 0 \end{pmatrix} = (1 - \lambda) \begin{pmatrix} u_1 \\ u_2 \end{pmatrix} + \begin{pmatrix} -u_2^3 \\ u_1^3 \end{pmatrix}. \tag{11.3}$$

Multiplying the first component of (11.3) by u_2, the second by u_1, and subtracting yields $u_1^4 + u_2^4 = 0$ for any solution (λ, u). Hence (11.3) has only trivial solutions. Thus $\mu = 1 \in \sigma(L)$ but $(1, (0, 0))$ is not a bifurcation point. Surprisingly, however, if variational structure is present, $\mu \in \sigma(L)$ is not only necessary but is also, modulo some additional technicalities, a sufficient condition for bifurcation to occur. To be more precise, suppose E is a Hilbert space, $\Phi \in C^1(E, \mathbf{R})$, and D denotes the duality mapping between E^* and E. Then $D\Phi'\colon E \to E$.

THEOREM 11.4. *Suppose E is a real Hilbert space and $I \in C^2(E, \mathbf{R})$ with $D\Phi'(u) = Lu + H(u)$, where $L \in \mathcal{L}(E, E)$ is symmetric and $H(u) = o(\|u\|)$ as*

$u \to 0$. *If $\mu \in \sigma(L)$ is an isolated eigenvalue of finite multiplicity, then $(\mu, 0)$ is a bifurcation point for*

$$\mathcal{F}(\lambda, u) \equiv D\Phi'(u) - \lambda u = Lu + H(u) - \lambda u.$$

Moreover there is an $r_0 > 0$ such that

(i) *for each $r \in (0, r_0)$ there exist at least two distinct solutions $(\lambda_i(r), u_i(r))$, $i = 1, 2$, of $\mathcal{F} = 0$ having $\|u_i\| = r$ and $|\lambda_i - \mu|$ small.*

(ii) *As $r \to 0$, $(\lambda_i(r), u_i(r)) \to (\mu, 0)$.*

REMARK 11.5. Actually I need only be defined on a neighborhood of 0 in E. Theorem 11.4 is due independently to Böhme [**Bö**] and Marino [**Ma**]. Aside from smoothness considerations, it generalizes an earlier result of Krasnoselski [**K**]. Minimax methods are not needed to prove Theorem 11.4. A standard construction from bifurcation theory converts the problem of finding zeros of $\mathcal{F}$ to a finite dimensional problem in $\mathbf{R} \times N(L - \mu\,\text{id})$, where $N(A)$ denotes the null space of a linear operator A. The latter problem will be solved by obtaining the maximum and minimum of a functional defined on a spherelike manifold in $N(L - \mu\,\text{id})$.

The proof of Theorem 11.4 begins with the finite dimensional reduction mentioned above. Let $N \equiv N(L - \mu\,\text{id})$ and let $N^\perp$ denote its orthogonal complement. Then $E = N \oplus N^\perp$ and if $u \in E$, $u \equiv v + w \in N \oplus N^\perp$. Let P and $P^\perp$ denote respectively the orthogonal projectors of E onto N, $N^\perp$. We seek solutions of the equation

$$Lu + H(u) = \lambda u \tag{11.6}$$

near $(\mu, 0)$. Using P and $P^\perp$, (11.6) is equivalent to the pair of equations

$$Lv + PH(v + w) = \lambda v, \tag{11.7}$$

$$Lw + P^\perp H(v + w) = \lambda w. \tag{11.8}$$

Set

$$F(\lambda, v, w) \equiv (L - \lambda\,\text{id})w + P^\perp H(v + w).$$

The hypotheses on I imply $F \in C^1(\mathbf{R} \times N \times N^\perp, N^\perp)$. Clearly $F(\mu, 0, 0) = 0$. Let $F_w(\mu, v, w)$ denote the Fréchet derivative of F with respect to w. Then $F_w(\mu, 0, 0) = L - \mu\,\text{id}$, an isomorphism of $N^\perp$ onto $N^\perp$. Therefore by the Implicit Function Theorem, there is a neighborhood, $\mathcal{O}$, of $(\mu, 0)$ in $\mathbf{R} \times N$ and a mapping $\varphi \in C^1(\mathcal{O}, N^\perp)$ such that $\varphi(\mu, 0) = 0$ and the zeros of F near $(\mu, 0)$ are given by $\{(\lambda, v, \varphi(\lambda, v)) | (\lambda, v) \in \mathcal{O}\}$. Thus to solve (11.6) near $(\mu, 0)$, it suffices to solve the *finite dimensional problem*

$$Lv + PH(v + \varphi(\lambda, v)) = \lambda v,$$

or equivalently since $Lv = \mu v$,

$$(\lambda - \mu)v = PH(v + \varphi(\lambda, v)). \tag{11.9}$$

This reduction is called the *Method of Lyapunov-Schmidt.*

Before continuing further, two useful estimates should be pointed out. Since $L-\lambda\,\mathrm{id}$ is an isomorphism of $N^\perp$ to $N^\perp$ for all λ near μ, (11.8) can be rewritten as

$$\varphi(\lambda, v) = -(L-\lambda\,\mathrm{id})^{-1}P^\perp H(v+\varphi(\lambda, v)). \tag{11.10}$$

Since $H(\lambda, u) = o(\|u\|)$ as $u \to 0$, (11.10) shows

$$\varphi(\lambda, v) = o(\|v+\varphi(\lambda, v)\|)$$

as $v \to 0$ and therefore

$$\varphi(\lambda, v) = o(\|v\|) \tag{11.11}$$

as $v \to 0$ uniformly for λ near μ. Differentiating (11.8) with respect to λ gives

$$(L-\lambda\,\mathrm{id} + P^\perp H'(v+\varphi(\lambda, v)))\frac{\partial\varphi}{\partial\lambda}(\lambda, v) = \varphi(\lambda, v). \tag{11.12}$$

Since $H'(0) = 0$, (11.11) and (11.12) imply

$$\frac{\partial\varphi}{\partial\lambda}(\lambda, v) = o(\|v\|) \tag{11.13}$$

as $v \to 0$ uniformly for λ near μ.

The next step in the proof of Theorem 11.4 is to find λ as a function of v near $(\mu, 0)$. By (11.9),

$$(\lambda-\mu)\|v\|^2 = (H(v+\varphi(\lambda, v)), v),$$

or

$$\lambda - \mu - \frac{(H(v+\varphi(\lambda, v)), v)}{\|v\|^2} = 0 \tag{11.14}$$

for $v \neq 0$ and (λ, v) near $(\mu, 0)$. Define $G(\lambda, v)$ to be the left-hand side of (11.14) and $G(\lambda, 0) \equiv \lambda - \mu$. The estimates (11.11), (11.13) and properties of H show G is continuous from a neighborhood of $(\mu, 0)$ in $\mathbf{R} \times N$ to $\mathbf{R}$, $G(\mu, 0) = 0$, G is continuously differentiable in λ near $(\mu, 0)$, and also with respect to v for $v \neq 0$. Since $\partial G(\mu, 0)/\partial\lambda = 1$, a stronger version of the Implicit Function Theorem [**Di**] implies the zeros of G near $(\mu, 0)$ are given by $\lambda = \psi(v)$, where ψ is continuous in a neighborhood of 0, $\psi(0) = \mu$, and $\psi(v)$ is continuously differentiable in a deleted neighborhood of 0.

Now set $\chi(v) = \varphi(\psi(v), v)$. Then χ is a continuous map of a neighborhood of 0 in N to $N^\perp$ and is continuously differentiable in a deleted neighborhood of 0. Moreover $\chi(v) = o(\|v\|)$ as $v \to 0$. For our later purposes, the behavior of χ' near 0 must be studied. By (11.8) for $z \in \mathbf{N}$ and small $t \in \mathbf{R}$,

$$(L-\psi(v+tz)\mathrm{id})\chi(v+tz) + P^\perp H(v+tz+\chi(v+tz)) = 0. \tag{11.15}$$

Differentiating (11.15) at $t = 0$ gives

$$\begin{aligned}(L-\psi(v)\mathrm{id} + P^\perp H'(v+\chi(v)))\chi'(v)z \\ = (\psi'(v), z)\chi(v) - P^\perp H'(v+\chi(v))z.\end{aligned} \tag{11.16}$$

Similarly (11.14) yields

$$(11.17)\qquad \begin{aligned}(\psi'(v), z) = \|v\|^{-2}[(H'(v+\chi(v))(z+\chi'(v)z), v) + (H(v+\chi(v)), z)] \\ - 2(H(v+\chi(v)), v)(v, z)\|v\|^{-4}.\end{aligned}$$

Consequently since $H'(0) = 0$, by (11.16)–(11.17), for v near 0, $v \neq 0$,

$$(11.18)\qquad \begin{aligned}\|\chi'(v)z\| &\le \text{const}[|(\psi'(v), z)|\,\|\chi(v)\| + \|H'(v+\chi(v))\|\,\|z\|] \\ &\le \text{const}\left\{\left[\frac{\|H'(v+\chi(v))\|}{\|v\|}(\|z\| + \|\chi'(v)z\|)\right.\right. \\ &\qquad \left. + \frac{\|H(v+\chi(v))\|}{\|v\|^2}\|z\|\right]\|\chi(v)\| \\ &\qquad \left. + \|P^\perp H'(v+\chi(v))\|\,\|z\|\right\} \\ &= o(1)\|z\| + o(1)\|\chi'(v)z\|\end{aligned}$$

as $v \to 0$, $v \neq 0$, or

$$(11.19)\qquad \|\chi'(v)z\| = o(1)\|z\|$$

as $v \to 0$, $v \neq 0$. Equation (11.19) shows $\chi'(v)$ extends continuously to $v = 0$ and $\chi'(0) = 0$.

With these preliminaries in hand, the proof of Theorem 11.4 can be reduced to the study of a finite dimensional variational problem. Let $\mathcal{V}$ be a neighborhood of 0 in N in which ψ and χ are defined and C^1. Let $\mathcal{M} \equiv \{v + \chi(v) | v \in \mathcal{V}\}$. Then $\mathcal{M}$ is a C^1 manifold of dimension $n \equiv \dim N$ in E. Let $\varepsilon > 0$ and set $\mathcal{D}_\varepsilon \equiv \mathcal{M} \cap \partial B_\varepsilon$ so for small ε, $\mathcal{D}_\varepsilon$ is a compact C^1, $n-1$ manifold. Consider $I|_{\mathcal{D}_\varepsilon}$. This functional possesses at least two distinct critical points corresponding to the maximum and minimum of I on $\mathcal{D}_\varepsilon$. We claim that at any critical point u of $I|_{\mathcal{D}_\varepsilon}$, $I'(u) = \lambda u$, where $u = v + \chi(v)$ and $\lambda = \psi(v)$. Assuming this for the moment, observe that as $\varepsilon \to 0$, if $v_\varepsilon \in \mathcal{D}_\varepsilon$, then $v_\varepsilon \to 0$. Therefore $v_\varepsilon + \chi(v_\varepsilon) \to 0$ and $\psi(v_\varepsilon) \to \mu$. Thus the proof of Theorem 11.4 will be complete once the above claim is verified.

If u is a critical point of $I|_{\mathcal{D}_\varepsilon}$, then

$$(11.20)\qquad I'(u)\varphi = 0$$

for all $\varphi \in T\mathcal{D}_{\varepsilon u}$, where TM_x denotes the tangent manifold to manifold M at the point x. Now

$$T\mathcal{D}_{\varepsilon x} = T\mathcal{M}_x \cap T(\partial B_\varepsilon)_x$$

and

$$T(\partial B_\varepsilon)_x = \{\varphi \in E | (\varphi, x) = 0\}.$$

Therefore

$$T\mathcal{D}_{\varepsilon x} = \{\varphi \in T\mathcal{M}_x | (\varphi, x) = 0\}.$$

Equation (11.20) readily implies

$$(11.21)\qquad (DI'(u) - \varepsilon^{-2}(DI'(u), u)u, \varphi) = 0$$

for all $\varphi \in \text{span}\{u, T\mathcal{D}_{\varepsilon u}\}$. We will show that (11.21) yields $I'(u) = \lambda u$, where $u = v + \chi(v)$ and $\lambda = \psi(v)$. Since $u \in \mathcal{M}$ implies $u = v + \chi(v)$, where $v \in \mathcal{V}$, the construction of χ shows $P^\perp DI'(u) = \psi(v)\chi(v)$. Therefore

$$(11.22) \qquad (DI'(u), \chi(v)) = \psi(v)\|\chi(v)\|^2.$$

The construction of ψ further implies

$$(11.23) \qquad (\psi(v) - \mu)\|v\|^2 = (DH(u), v).$$

Recalling that $\mu\|v\|^2 = (Lv, v)$, (11.22)–(11.23) yield

$$(11.24) \qquad (DI'(u), u) = \psi(v)\|u\|^2 = \psi(v)\varepsilon^2$$

for $u \in \mathcal{D}_\varepsilon$. Therefore

$$\psi(v) = \varepsilon^{-2}(DI'(u), u) = \lambda(v)$$

for all $v \in \mathcal{D}_\varepsilon$. Comparing this to (11.21) shows

$$(11.25) \qquad (DI'(u) - \psi(v)u, \varphi) = 0$$

for all $\varphi \in \text{span}\{u, T\mathcal{D}_{\varepsilon u}\}$. By (11.8), $P^\perp(DI'(u) - \lambda u) = 0$ so (11.25) gives

$$(11.26) \qquad (DI'(u) - \psi(v)u, \varphi) = 0$$

for all $\varphi \in \text{span}\{u, T\mathcal{D}_{\varepsilon u}, N^\perp\} \equiv W$.

We will show $W = E$ and therefore $DI'(u) = \lambda u$. To prove this, note first that $u = v + \chi'(u)v$ for some $v \in \mathcal{V}$ and $\chi'(v) \in N^\perp$. Therefore $W = \text{span}\{v, T\mathcal{D}_{\varepsilon u}, N^\perp\}$. Let $v_1, \ldots, v_{n-1}$ be a basis for $T\mathcal{D}_{\varepsilon u}$. To get a basis for $T\mathcal{M}_u$, we supplement these vectors by a vector v_n. Since $T\mathcal{M}_u = \{x + \chi'(v)x | x \in N\}$, we have

$$(11.27) \qquad v + \chi'(v)v = \sum_{i=1}^{n} \beta_i v_i.$$

Note that $\beta_n \neq 0$ in (11.27) for otherwise, $v + \chi'(v)v \in T\mathcal{D}_{\varepsilon u}$ and therefore

$$(11.28) \qquad (v + \chi'(v)v, u) = 0 = \|v\|^2 + (\chi'(v)v, \chi(v)) = \|v\|^2 + o(\|v\|^2)$$

for v near 0. Hence $v = 0$ if $\|v\|$ is small, contrary to $\|u\| = \|v + \chi(v)\| = \varepsilon$. Thus $\beta_n \neq 0$. Solving for v_n in (11.27) shows that

$$(11.29) \qquad v_n \in \text{span}\{v, T_{\varepsilon u}, N^\perp\} = W.$$

Finally observe that if $y \in E$,

$$\begin{aligned} y = (P + \chi'(v)P)y + (P^\perp - \chi'(v)Py) &\in \text{span}\{T\mathcal{M}_u, N^\perp\} \\ &= \text{span}\{v_n, T\mathcal{D}_{\varepsilon u}, N^\perp\} \subset W \end{aligned}$$

via (11.29). Therefore $W = E$ and the proof of Theorem 11.4 is complete.

COROLLARY 11.30. *If I is even and $\dim N = n$, the equation $DI'(u) = \lambda u$ possesses at least n distinct pairs of solutions $(\lambda_j(r), \pm u_j(r))$, $1 \le j \le n$, such that $\|u_j(r)\| = r$. Moreover $\lambda_j(r) \to \mu$ as $r \to 0$.*

PROOF. If I is even, φ and χ are odd functions, $\mathcal{D}_\varepsilon$ is a symmetric set, and $I|_{\mathcal{D}_\varepsilon}$ is even. A slight modification of the proof of Theorem 8.1 then gives the corollary. We shall not carry out the details.

We will briefly sketch an application of Theorem 11.4 to a bifurcation problem for a semilinear elliptic partial differential equation. Consider

$$\begin{aligned} -\Delta u &= \lambda(a(x)u + p(x,u)), \qquad x \in \Omega, \\ u &= 0, \qquad x \in \partial\Omega, \end{aligned} \tag{11.31}$$

where $p \in C^1(\overline{\Omega}, \mathbf{R})$ and satisfies (p_3) and a is as in (2.40). Let $\chi(\xi) \in C^\infty(\mathbf{R}, \mathbf{R})$ satisfy $\chi(\xi) = 1$ for $|\xi| \le 1$, $\chi(\xi) = 0$ for $|\xi| \ge 2$, and $0 \le \chi(\xi) \le 1$ for all ξ. Define

$$\tilde{p}(x,\xi) = \chi(\xi)p(x,\xi) + (1 - \chi(\xi)).$$

Then $\tilde{p} \in C^1$, and satisfies (p_2) (with $s = 0$) and (p_3). Set

$$I(u) = \int_\Omega (\tfrac{1}{2}au^2 + \tilde{P}(x,u))\,dx$$

with $u \in E = W_0^{1,2}(\Omega)$ as usual. The properties of $\tilde{p}$ and Proposition B.34 imply $I \in C^2(E, \mathbf{R})$. The argument of Theorem 8.17 shows that a critical point of $I|_{\partial B_r}$ satisfies

$$\int_\Omega (au + \tilde{p}(x,u))\varphi\,dx = \nu \int \nabla u \cdot \nabla \varphi\,dx$$

for some ν and all $\varphi \in E$, i.e. u is a weak solution of (11.31) (for $\tilde{p}$) on ∂B_r with $\lambda = \nu^{-1}$. In terms of Theorem 11.4, using (p_3) it is not difficult to check that

$$H(u)\varphi = \int_\Omega p(x,u)\varphi\,dx,$$

L is defined by

$$(Lu, \varphi) = \int_\Omega au\varphi\,dx,$$

and $\sigma(L) = \{\mu \in \mathbf{R} | au - \mu\Delta u = 0 \text{ for some } u \not\equiv 0,\ u \in E\}$, i.e. $\sigma(L) = \{\lambda_j^{-1} | \lambda_j$ is an eigenvalue of (2.40)$\}$. Since these eigenvalues are of finite multiplicity and isolated, by Theorem 11.4, each eigenvalue of (2.40) provides a bifurcation point for (11.31) (for $\tilde{p}$). Arguments from elliptic regularity theory show if r is small enough, $\|u\|_{L^\infty(\Omega)} < 1$ and therefore $\tilde{p}(x,u) = p(x,u)$. Thus we have shown

THEOREM 11.32. *If $p \in C^1(\overline{\Omega}, \mathbf{R})$ and satisfies (p_3), every eigenvalue λ_j of (2.40) gives rise to a bifurcation point $(\lambda_j, 0)$ of (11.31).*

REMARK 11.33. If p is odd, Corollary 11.30 can be used to say more about the number of solutions of (11.31) near $(\lambda_j, 0)$.

Our final result in this chapter is a variation on Theorem 11.4 where we seek solutions of

$$(11.34)\qquad Lu + H(u) = \lambda u$$

as functions of λ rather than of $r = \|u\|$. This is a somewhat more subtle situation than the case treated in Theorem 11.4 and involves ideas of a minimax nature.

THEOREM 11.35 [**R3**]. *Under the hypotheses of Theorem* 11.4, *either*

(i) $(\mu, 0)$ *is not an isolated solution of* (11.34) *in* $\{\mu\} \times E$, *or*

(ii) *there is a one sided neighborhood* Λ *of* μ *such that for all* $\lambda \in \Lambda \setminus \{\mu\}$, (11.34) *possesses at least two distinct nontrivial solutions, or*

(iii) *there is a neighborhood* Λ *of* μ *such that for all* $\lambda \in \Lambda \setminus \{\mu\}$, (11.34) *possesses at least one nontrivial solution.*

PROOF. By the proof of Theorem 11.4, (11.34) is equivalent to (11.9) where $\varphi(\lambda, v) \in C^1$ and $\varphi(\lambda, v) = o(\|v\|)$ as $v \to 0$ uniformly for λ near μ. Define

$$g(\lambda, v) \equiv I(v + \varphi(\lambda, v)) - (\lambda/2)(\|v\|^2 + \|\varphi(\lambda, v)\|^2).$$

Then g is C^1 for v near 0 in N. Letting h denote the primitive of H with $h(0) = 0$ shows

$$(11.36)\qquad g(\lambda, v) = \frac{\mu - \lambda}{2}\|v\|^2 + \frac{1}{2}((L - \lambda\,\mathrm{id})\varphi, \varphi) + h(v + \varphi).$$

We claim critical points of $g(\lambda, \cdot)$ near $v = 0$ are solutions of (11.9). Indeed at a critical point of g we have

$$(11.37)\qquad \begin{aligned} \left.\frac{d}{dt} g(\lambda, v + t\hat{v})\right|_{t=0} &= (g_v(\lambda, v), \hat{v}) \\ &= I_v(v + \varphi(\lambda, v))\hat{v} + I_w(v + \varphi(\lambda, v))\varphi_v(\lambda, v)\hat{v} \\ &\quad - \lambda[(v, \hat{v}) + (\varphi(\lambda, u), \varphi_v(\lambda, v)\hat{v})]. \end{aligned}$$

Since by (11.7),

$$(DI_w(v + \varphi(\lambda, v)) - \lambda\varphi, \hat{w}) = 0$$

for all $\hat{w} \in N^\perp$, (11.37) simplifies to

$$0 = (g_v(\lambda, v), \hat{v}) = (DI_v - \lambda v, \hat{v})$$

for all $\hat{v} \in N$ which is equivalent to (11.9).

Now in order to prove Theorem 11.35, we need only analyze the critical points of $g(\lambda, \cdot)$ near 0 for λ near μ. The form of g implies $v = 0$ is a critical point of $g(\lambda, \cdot)$ for all λ near μ. If 0 is not an isolated critical point of $g(\mu, \cdot)$, then alternative (i) of Theorem 11.35 holds. Thus for what follows we assume 0 is an isolated critical point of $g(\mu, \cdot)$. Consequently 0 is either (a) a strict local maximum or minimum for $g(\mu, \cdot)$, or (b) $g(\mu, \cdot)$ takes on both positive and negative values near 0. The former possibility leads to alternative (ii) and the latter to alternative (iii) of Theorem 11.35. Before verifying these statements, note that

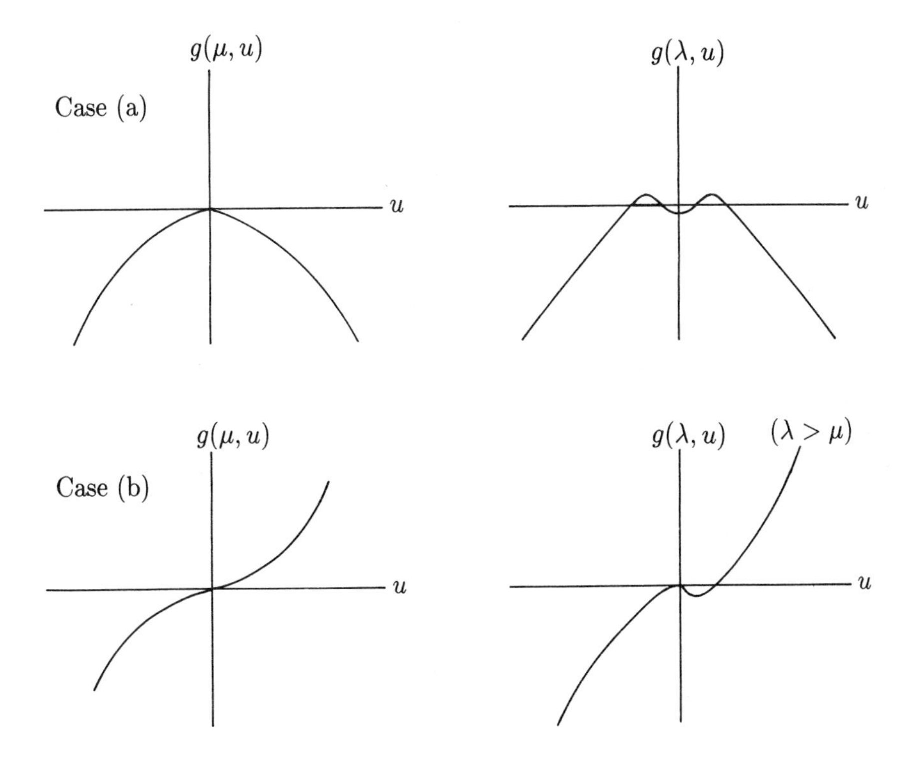

for the special case of $\dim N = 1$, one can use the shown figures as a basis for a proof.

Case (a): 0 *is a strict local maximum or minimum for* $g(\mu, \cdot)$. We will assume that 0 is a strict local maximum for $g(\mu, \cdot)$. Replace g by $-g$ to handle the case of a strict local minimum. Since $g(\mu, 0) = 0$, for $r > 0$ and small, there exists a $\beta > 0$ such that $g(\mu, \cdot) \le -2\beta$ on ∂B_r. (Here and for the remainder of this section the sets we are working with lie in N.) Therefore for λ near μ, $g(\lambda, \cdot) \le -\beta$ on ∂B_r. By (11.36) and previous remarks,

$$g(\lambda, v) = \frac{\mu - \lambda}{2} \|v\|^2 + o(\|v\|^2) \tag{11.38}$$

as $v \to 0$. Hence $g(\lambda, u) > 0$ if $\lambda < \mu$ and $0 \neq v$ is sufficiently small. In particular there exists a $\rho \in (0, r)$ such that $g(\lambda, v) \ge (\mu - \lambda)4^{-1}\rho^2 \equiv \alpha(\lambda)$ for $v \in \partial B_\rho$. Let

$$\bar{c}(\lambda) \equiv \max_{v \in B_r} g(\lambda, v). \tag{11.39}$$

Then for $\lambda < \mu$ and λ sufficiently close to μ, $\bar{c}(\lambda) \ge \alpha(\lambda) > 0$ and is a critical value of $g(\lambda, \cdot)$. Moreover $g(\lambda, \cdot)$ satisfies hypotheses (I_1) and (I_2) of the Mountain Pass Theorem, the latter with e being any point on ∂B_r. Theorem 2.2 cannot be applied directly since $g(\lambda, \cdot)$ is only defined near 0 in N. However since $\alpha(\lambda) > 0 > -\beta$, it is easy (via the proof of the Deformation Theorem) to construct a map $\eta \in C([0,1] \times \overline{B}_r, \overline{B}_r)$ such that $\eta(t,\cdot) = \text{id}$ on ∂B_r and η has the properties of Theorem A.4 relative to B_r. Consequently if

$$\Gamma = \{h \in C([0,1], \overline{B}_r) | h(0) = 0 \text{ and } h(1) \in \partial B_r\}$$

and

$$\underline{c}(\lambda) = \inf_{h \in \Gamma} \max_{t \in [0,1]} g(\lambda, h(t)), \tag{11.40}$$

the proof of Theorem 2.2 shows $\underline{c}(\lambda) \geq \alpha(\lambda) > 0$ is also a critical value of $g(\lambda,\cdot)$ for $\lambda < \mu$ and near μ. If $\underline{c}(\lambda) < \overline{c}(\lambda)$, it is clear that (11.34) has two distinct nontrivial solutions. If $\underline{c}(\lambda) = \overline{c}(\lambda)$, (11.39)–(11.40) show $\overline{c}(\lambda)$ equals the maximum of $g(\lambda,\cdot)$ over every curve in Γ. Therefore the set of points in B_r at which $g(\lambda,\cdot)$ achieves its maximum in B_r separates 0 and ∂B_r. Consequently this critical set contains the boundary of a neighborhood of 0 in N. In any event we see Case (a) implies alternative (ii) of Theoem 11.35.

Case (b): *$g(\mu,\cdot)$ takes on both positive and negative values near* 0. This case is more subtle than the previous one. Again the idea is to reduce the proof to an argument of "mountain pass" type but a more complicated construction is required.

To begin, the computation in (11.37) shows

$$g_v(\lambda, v) = (\mu - \lambda)v + PH(v + \varphi(\lambda, v))$$

which is C^1 in (λ, v). Hence the negative gradient flow corresponding to $g(\mu,\cdot)$:

$$\frac{d\psi}{dt} = -g_v(\mu, \psi), \qquad \psi(0, v) = v, \tag{11.41}$$

has a unique (local in t) solution for all v near 0 in N. Let $\overline{B}_r$ be a small ball in which this flow is defined. Set

$$S^+ \equiv \{x \in B_r | \psi(t,x) \in B_r \text{ for all } t > 0\}$$

and

$$S^- \equiv \{x \in B_r | \psi(t,x) \in B_r \text{ for all } t < 0\}.$$

LEMMA 11.42. *S^+ and S^- are nonempty.*

PROOF. We will only verify the S^+ case. Let $(x_m) \subset B_r$ be a sequence such that $x_m \to 0$ as $m \to \infty$ and $g(\mu, x_m) > 0$. Consider $\psi(t, x_m)$. By assumption, $g_v(\mu, v) \neq 0$ in $\overline{B}_r$ for $v \neq 0$. If for fixed m, the orbit $\psi(t, x_m)$ remained in $\overline{B}_r$ for all $t < 0$, it would have to converge to a critical point of $g(\mu,\cdot)$ with positive critical value. Since this is impossible, there exists a smallest $t_m < 0$ such that $\psi(t_m, x_m) \equiv y_m \in \partial B_r$. Since $x_m \to 0$ as $m \to \infty$ and $g_v(\mu, 0) = 0$, $t_m \to -\infty$ as $m \to \infty$. Let y be a limit point of (y_m). Then $\psi(t, y) \in B_r$ for all $t > 0$ so $y \in S^+$.

REMARK 11.43. Since $H(u) = o(\|u\|)$ as $u \to 0$, the matrix $g_{vv}(\mu, v)$ vanishes at $v = 0$. If it were nonsingular, S^+ and S^- would be respectively the stable and unstable manifolds at 0 of the flow given by $g_v(\mu,\cdot)$.

PROPOSITION 11.44. *There exists a neighborhood Q of 0 in N and constants $c^+ > 0 > c^-$ such that $Q \subset B_r$ and $v \in \partial Q$ implies either*
(i) $g(\mu, v) = c^+$, *or*
(ii) $g(\mu, v) = c^-$, *or*
(iii) $\psi(t, v) \in \partial Q$ *for all t near* 0.

Assuming Proposition 11.44 for the moment, we can complete the proof of Case (b). Let $T^- = g(\mu, \cdot)^{-1}(c^-) \cap S^-$. The construction of S^- and Q shows $T^- \neq \emptyset$. Set

$$\Gamma \equiv \{h \in C([0,1], Q) | h(0) = 0, h(1) \in T^-\}.$$

Define

$$c(\lambda) = \inf_{h \in \Gamma} \max_{t \in [0,1]} g(\lambda, h(t)). \tag{11.45}$$

Letting $\lambda < \mu$ and choosing ρ as following (11.38) shows $c(\lambda) \geq \alpha(\lambda) > 0$. We claim $c(\lambda)$ is a critical value of $g(\lambda, \cdot)$. Indeed (A.1) shows $-g_v(\mu, v)$ is a pseudo-gradient vector for $-g_v(\lambda, v)$ for all $v \in \partial Q$. This permits a modification of the proof of the Deformation Theorem to find $\eta \in C([0,1] \times Q, Q)$ having the usual properties and the use of $\eta(1, \cdot)$ in the usual fashion to conclude that $c(\lambda)$ is a critical value of $g(\lambda, \cdot)$.

If $\lambda > \mu$, the same argument works on replacing g by $-g$.

It remains to construct the set Q. Let $A_c \equiv \{v \in N | g(\mu, v) \leq c\}$.

LEMMA 11.46. *There is an $\varepsilon > 0$ such that if $c \equiv \max_{v \in B_\varepsilon} g(\mu, v)$ and $x \in B_\varepsilon \setminus S^-$, then as $t \to -\infty$, the orbit $\psi(t, x)$ leaves $A_c \cap B_r$ via $A_c \setminus \partial B_r$.*

PROOF. If not, there are sequences $\varepsilon_m \to 0$, $x_m \in B_{\varepsilon_m} \setminus S^-$, and $t_m < 0$ such that $z_m \equiv \psi(t_m, x_m) \in \partial B_r$ and

$$\min_{v \in B_{\varepsilon_m}} g(\mu, v) \leq g(\mu, z_m) \leq \max_{v \in B_{\varepsilon_m}} g(\mu, v).$$

Therefore along a subsequence, $z_m \to z \in \partial B_r$ and $g(\mu, z) = 0$. Let $\tau_m < 0$ denote the time of final exit of $\psi(t, x_m)$ from B_{ε_1} as $t \to -\infty$ and consider $\psi(t, x_m)$ for $t \in (t_m, \tau_m)$. Since $\|g_v(\mu, v)\|$ is bounded away from 0 in $\overline{B}_r \setminus B_{\varepsilon_1}$, (11.41) shows that

$$\delta_m \equiv g(\mu, z_m) - g(\mu, \psi(\tau_m, x_m)) \geq \text{const} > 0$$

if $|t_m - \tau_m|$ is bounded away from 0. But our above remarks show $\delta_m \to 0$ as $m \to \infty$ so $|t_m - \tau_m| \to 0$ as $m \to \infty$, i.e. the time it takes the orbit to go from $\psi(\tau_m, x_m)$ on $\partial B_{\varepsilon_1}$ to z_m on ∂B_r tends to 0. However this cannot happen since $g_v(\mu, v)$ is bounded away from infinity. Therefore there exists an ε as desired.

An obvious consequence of Lemma 11.46 is

COROLLARY 11.47. *There is an $\varepsilon > 0$ such that if*

$$c^+ = \max_{v \in B_\varepsilon} g(\mu, v), \qquad c^- = \min_{v \in B_\varepsilon} g(\mu, v),$$

and $x \in B_\varepsilon \setminus S^-$, *as* $t \to -\infty$ *the orbit* $\psi(t,x)$ *leaves* $A_{c^+} \cap \partial B_r$ *via* A_{c^+} *and if* $x \in B_\varepsilon \setminus S^+$, *as* $t \to \infty$ *the orbit* $\psi(t,x)$ *leaves* $A_{c^-} \cap B_r$ *via* A_{c^-}.

Now let ε be as given by Corollary 11.47. For each $x \in B_\varepsilon \setminus S^-$, there is a corresponding $t^-(x)$ such that $g(\mu, \psi(t^-(x), x)) = c^+$ and for each $x \in B_\varepsilon \setminus S^+$, there is a $t^+(x)$ such that $g(\mu, \psi(t^+(x), x)) = c^-$. If $x \in S^+$, set $t^-(x) = -\infty$; if $x \in S^+$, set $t^+(x) = \infty$. Finally define

$$Q \equiv \{\psi(t,x) | x \in B_\varepsilon \text{ and } t^-(x) < t < t^+(x)\}.$$

PROOF OF PROPOSITION 11.44. Clearly $B_\varepsilon \subset Q$. If $z \in Q \setminus B_\varepsilon$, $z = \psi(t,x)$ for some $x \in B_\varepsilon$ and $t \in (t^-(x), t^+(x))$. Therefore for δ small, $\psi(t, B_\delta(x)) \subset Q$ and is a neighborhood of z so Q is a neighborhood of 0. Let $v \in \partial Q$ and suppose $g(\mu, v) \neq c^+$ or c^-. Consider $\mathcal{O}_v \equiv \{\psi(t,v) | t \in \mathbf{R}\}$. Since $v = \lim_{m\to\infty} v_m$, where $v_m \in Q$, and $\mathcal{O}_{v_m} \cap B_\varepsilon \neq \varnothing$, there exists an $x \in \mathcal{O}_v \cap \overline{B}_\varepsilon$. Therefore $x = \psi(\tau, v)$ for some $\tau \in \mathbf{R}$ and $v = \psi(-\tau, x)$, where $-\tau \in (t^-(x), t^+(x))$ since $g(\mu, v) \in (c^-, c^+)$. Hence $x \in \partial B_\varepsilon$ for otherwise $v \in Q$. Moreover $g(\mu, \psi(s,v)) \in (c^-, c^+)$ for s near 0. Since $\psi(s,v) = \psi(s-\tau, x)$, it is clear that $\psi(s,v) \in \partial Q$. Indeed $\psi(s,v) = \lim_{m\to\infty} \psi(s-\tau, x_m)$, where $x_m \in B_\varepsilon$, $x_m \to x$, and therefore $s - \tau \in (t^-(x_m), t^+(x_m))$. The proof is complete.

REMARK 11.48. If I is even, a much stronger result than Theorem 11.35 holds (see [**FR**]).

Appendix A

The goal of Appendixes A and B is to prove some results that were required earlier which are rather technical in nature. In particular in this appendix we will prove a fairly general version of the Deformation Theorem. Thus let E be a real Banach space, $U \subset E$, and $I \in C^1(U, \mathbf{R})$. Then $v \in E$ is called a *pseudo-gradient vector for I at $u \in U$* [**P2**] if:

$$\text{(A.1)} \qquad \begin{aligned} &\text{(i)} \quad \|v\| \leq 2\|I'(u)\|, \\ &\text{(ii)} \quad I'(u)v \geq \|I'(u)\|^2. \end{aligned}$$

In the future pseudo-gradient will be denoted by p.g. for short. Note that a p.g. vector is not unique in general and any convex combination of p.g. vectors for I at u is also a p.g. vector for I at u.

Let $I \in C^1(E, \mathbf{R})$ and $\tilde{E} \equiv \{u \in E | I'(u) \neq 0\}$. Then $V \colon \tilde{E} \to E$ is called a *p.g. vector field on $\tilde{E}$* if V is locally Lipschitz continuous and $V(x)$ is a p.g. vector for I for all $x \in \tilde{E}$.

LEMMA A.2. *If $I \in C^1(E, \mathbf{R})$, there exists a p.g. vector field for I on $\tilde{E}$.*

PROOF. For each $u \in \tilde{E}$, we can find a vector $w \in E$ such that $\|w\| = 1$ and $I'(u)w > \frac{2}{3}\|I'(u)\|$. Then $z = \frac{3}{2}\|I'(u)\|w$ is a p.g. vector for I at u with strict inequality in (i) and (ii) of (A.1). The continuity of I' then shows z is a p.g. vector for all $v \in N_u$, an open neighborhood of u. Since $\{N_u | u \in \tilde{E}\}$ is an open covering of $\tilde{E}$, it possesses a locally finite refinement which will be denoted by $\{M_j\}$. Let $\rho_j(x)$ denote the distance from x to the complement of M_j. Then $\rho_j(x)$ is Lipschitz continuous and $\rho_j(x) = 0$ if $x \notin M_j$. Set

$$\beta_j(x) = \rho_j(x) \Big/ \sum_k \rho_k(x).$$

The denominator of β_j is only a finite sum since each $x \in E$ belongs to only finitely many sets M_k. Each of the sets M_j lies in some N_{u_j}. Let $z_j \equiv \frac{3}{2}\|I'(u_j)\|w_j$, a p.g. vector for I in M_j and set $V(x) \equiv \sum_j z_j \beta_j(x)$. Since $0 \leq \beta_j(x) \leq 1$ and $\sum_j \beta_j(x) = 1$, for each $x \in \tilde{E}$, $V(x)$ is a convex combination of p.g. vectors for I at x. Moreover V is locally Lipschitz continuous. The proof is complete.

COROLLARY A.3. *If $I(x)$ is even in x, I has a p.g. vector field on $\tilde{E}$ given by an odd function W.*

PROOF. Suppose I is even. Let V be as given by Lemma A.2 and set $W(x) = \frac{1}{2}(V(x) - V(-x))$. Then W is odd, locally Lipschitz continuous, and since $I'(x)$ is odd in x,

(i) $\|W(x)\| \le \frac{1}{2}(\|V(x)\| + \|V(-x)\|) \le 2\|I'(x)\|$,

(ii) $I'(x)W(x) = \frac{1}{2}I'(x)V(x) + \frac{1}{2}I'(-x)V(-x) \ge \|I'(x)\|^2$.

Recall that $A_s \equiv \{u \in E | I(u) \le s\}$ and $K_s \equiv \{u \in E | I(u) = s \text{ and } I'(u) = 0\}$. Now we will prove the following version of the Deformation Theorem (which in particular contains Proposition 2.1 as a very special case). See e.g. [**Br1**, **C**, **P1**, **S1**] for earlier such results.

THEOREM A.4. *Let E be a real Banach space and let $I \in C^1(E, \mathbf{R})$ and satisfy (PS). If $c \in R$, $\bar{\varepsilon} > 0$, and $\mathcal{O}$ is any neighborhood of K_c, then there exists an $\varepsilon \in (0, \bar{\varepsilon})$ and $\eta \in C([0,1] \times E, E)$ such that*

1° $\eta(0,u) = u$ for all $u \in E$.

2° $\eta(t,u) = u$ for all $t \in [0,1]$ if $I(u) \notin [c - \bar{\varepsilon}, c + \bar{\varepsilon}]$.

3° $\eta(t,u)$ is a homeomorphism of E onto E for each $t \in [0,1]$.

4° $\|\eta(t,u) - u\| \le 1$ for all $t \in [0,1]$ and $u \in E$.

5° $I(\eta(t,u)) \le I(u)$ for all $t \in [0,1]$ and $u \in E$.

6° $\eta(1, A_{c+\varepsilon} \setminus \mathcal{O}) \subset A_{c-\varepsilon}$.

7° If $K_c = \emptyset$, $\eta(1, A_{c+\varepsilon}) \subset A_{c-\varepsilon}$.

8° If $I(u)$ is even in u, $\eta(t,u)$ is odd in u.

PROOF. The function η will be constructed as the solution of a suitably modified negative gradient flow for I. A few preliminaries are needed before setting up this differential equation. By (PS), K_c is compact. Set $N_\delta \equiv \{u \in E | \, \|u - K_c\| < \delta\}$, where $\|u - K_c\|$ denotes the distance from u to K_c. Choosing δ suitably small, $N_\delta \subset \mathcal{O}$. Therefore it suffices to prove 6° with $\mathcal{O}$ replaced by N_δ. Note also that if $K_c = \emptyset$, $N_\delta = \emptyset$ so we get 7° instead.

We claim there are constants $b, \hat{\varepsilon} > 0$ such that

$$\|I'(u)\| \ge b \quad \text{for all } u \in A_{c+\hat{\varepsilon}} \setminus (A_{c-\hat{\varepsilon}} \cup N_{\delta/8}). \tag{A.5}$$

If not, there are sequences $b_n \to 0$, $\hat{\varepsilon}_n \to 0$, and $u_n \in A_{c+\hat{\varepsilon}_n} \setminus (A_{c-\hat{\varepsilon}_n} \cup N_{\delta/8})$ such that $\|I'(u_n)\| < b_n$. By (PS), a subsequence of u_n converges to $u \in K_c \setminus N_{\delta/8}$. But this latter set is empty. Hence there are constants $b, \hat{\varepsilon}$ as in (A.5). Since (A.5) still holds if $\hat{\varepsilon}$ is decreased, it can further be assumed that

$$0 < \hat{\varepsilon} < \min\left(\bar{\varepsilon}, \frac{b\delta}{32}, \frac{b^2}{2}, \frac{1}{8}\right). \tag{A.6}$$

Choosing any $\varepsilon \in (0, \hat{\varepsilon})$, define

$$A \equiv \{u \in E | I(u) \le c - \hat{\varepsilon}\} \cup \{u \in E | I(u) \ge c + \hat{\varepsilon}\}$$

and

$$B \equiv \{u \in E | c - \varepsilon \le I(u) \le c + \varepsilon\}.$$

Therefore $A \cap B = \emptyset$. Set

$$g(x) = \frac{\|x - A\|}{\|x - A\| + \|x - B\|}.$$

Then $g = 0$ on A, $g = 1$ on B, $0 \le g \le 1$, and g is Lipschitz continuous on E. Similarly there is a Lipschitz continuous function f on E such that $f = 1$ on $E \setminus N_{\delta/4}$, $f = 0$ on $N_{\delta/8}$, and $0 \le f \le 1$. Note that if I is even, A, B, and N_δ will be symmetric sets with respect to the origin and f and g are even functions. Next define $h(s) = 1$ if $s \in [0,1]$ and $h(s) = 1/s$ if $s \ge 1$. Since $I \in C^1(E, \mathbf{R})$, by Lemma A.2 and Corollary A.3, there exists a p.g. vector field V for I on $\tilde{E}$ with V odd if I is even. Finally set $W(x) = -f(x)g(x)h(\|V(x)\|)V(x)$ for $x \in \tilde{E}$ and $W(x) = 0$ otherwise. Then by construction, W is locally Lipschitz continuous on E with $0 \le \|W(x)\| \le 1$ and W is odd if I is even.

Now we can define the mapping η. Consider the Cauchy problem:

$$\frac{d\eta}{dt} = W(\eta), \qquad \eta(0,u) = u. \tag{A.7}$$

The basic existence-uniqueness theorem for ordinary differential equations implies that for each $u \in E$, (A.7) has a unique solution defined for t in a maximal interval $(t^-(u), t^+(u))$. We claim $t^\pm(u) = \pm\infty$. If not, say $t^+(u) < \infty$. Let $t_n \to t^+(u)$ with $t_n < t^+(u)$. Integrating (A.7) shows

$$\|\eta(t_{n+1}, u) - \eta(t_n, u)\| \le |t_{n+1} - t_n| \tag{A.8}$$

since $\|W(\cdot)\| \le 1$. But then $\eta(t_n, u)$ is a Cauchy sequence and hence converges to some $\overline{u}$ as $t_n \to t^+(u)$. The solution to (A.7) with $\overline{u}$ as initial data then furnishes a continuation of $\eta(t,u)$ to values of $t > t^+(u)$ contradicting the maximality of $t^+(u)$. Similarly $t^-(u) = -\infty$.

The continuous dependence of solutions of (A.7) on the initial data u implies $\eta \in C([0,1] \times E, E)$ and (A.7) implies 1° holds. Since $\overline{\varepsilon} > \hat{\varepsilon}$, $g(x) = 0$ on A so 2° is satisfied. The semigroup property for solutions of (A.7) gives 3°. Integrating (A.7) and using $\|W(\cdot)\| \le 1$ and 1° gives 4°. Above remarks on the oddness of W when I is even yield 8°. To verify 5°, note first that if $W(u) = 0$, $\eta(t,u) \equiv u$ is the solution of (A.7) (via uniqueness) so 5° is trivially satisfied. If $W(u) \ne 0$, $u \in \tilde{E}$ so $V(u)$ is defined as is $V(\eta(t,u))$ and

$$\begin{aligned} \frac{dI(\eta(t,u))}{dt} &= I'(\eta(t,u))\frac{d\eta}{dt} \\ &= -I'(\eta(t,u))f(\eta(t,u))g(\eta(t,u)) \\ &\quad \times h(\|V(\eta(t,u))\|)V(\eta(t,u)) \le 0 \end{aligned} \tag{A.9}$$

via (ii) of (A.1) and 5° follows for this case.

It remains only to verify 6° or a fortiori, $\eta(1, A_{c+\varepsilon} \setminus N_\delta) \subset A_{c-\varepsilon}$. If $u \in A_{c-\varepsilon}$, then $I(\eta(t,u)) \le c - \varepsilon$ by 5°. Thus we need only prove $u \in Y \equiv A_{c+\varepsilon} \setminus (A_{c-\varepsilon} \cup N_\delta)$ implies that $\eta(1,u) \in A_{c-\varepsilon}$. Let $u \in Y$. The reasoning that led to 5° showed

$$\frac{dI(\eta(t,u))}{dt} \le 0. \tag{A.10}$$

Since $g = 0$ on $A_{c-\hat{\varepsilon}}$, the orbit $\eta(t,u)$ cannot enter $A_{c-\hat{\varepsilon}}$. Therefore (A.10) implies

$$I(\eta(0,u)) - I(\eta(t,u)) \le \varepsilon + \hat{\varepsilon} < 2\hat{\varepsilon} \tag{A.11}$$

for all $t \ge 0$. Suppose that $u \in Y$ and $\eta(t,u) \in Z \equiv A_{c+\varepsilon} \setminus (A_{c-\varepsilon} \cup N_{\delta/2})$ for $s \in [0,t]$. This will certainly be the case for small t. Then for such s, $\eta(s,u) \in \tilde{E}$ (via (A.5)) and $f(\eta(s,u)) = 1 = g(\eta(s,u))$. By (A.11),

$$\begin{aligned}
2\hat{\varepsilon} &\ge \int_t^0 -I'(\eta(s,u))h(\|V(\eta(s,u))\|)V(\eta(s,u))\,ds \\
&= \int_0^t h(\|V(\eta(s,u))\|)I'(\eta(s,u))V(\eta(s,u))\,ds \\
&\ge \int_0^t h(\|V(\eta(s,u))\|)\|I'(\eta(s,u))\|^2\,ds \\
&\ge b\int_0^t h(\|V(\eta(s,u))\|)\|I'(\eta(s,u))\|\,dx \\
&\ge \frac{b}{2}\int_0^t h(\|V(\eta(s,u))\|)\|V(\eta(s,u))\|\,ds \\
&\ge \frac{b}{2}\left\|\int_0^t h(\|V(\eta(s,u))\|)V(\eta(s,u))\,ds\right\| \\
&= \frac{b}{2}\left\|\int_0^t W(\eta(s,u))\,ds\right\| = \frac{b}{2}\|\eta(t,u)-u\|,
\end{aligned} \tag{A.12}$$

where we successively used (A.1)(ii), (A.5), and (A.1)(i). Hence by (A.12) and (A.6),

$$\|\eta(t,u)-u\| \le \frac{4\hat{\varepsilon}}{b} < \frac{\delta}{8}.$$

Thus the orbit $\eta(t,u)$ cannot leave Z by entering $N_{\delta/2}$. Consequently the only way $\eta(t,u)$ can leave Z is to enter $A_{c-\varepsilon}$. We claim this occurs for some $t \in (0,1)$ thereby proving 6°. If not, $\eta(t,u) \in Z$ for all $t \in (0,1)$ and as in (A.12),

$$\frac{dI(\eta(t,u))}{dt} \le -h(\|V(\eta(t,u))\|)\|I'(\eta(t,u))\|^2. \tag{A.13}$$

If for some $t \in (0,1)$, $\|V(\eta(t,u))\| \le 1$, $h(\|V(\eta(t,u))\|) = 1$ and (A.5) and (A.13) imply

$$\frac{dI(\eta(t,u))}{dt} \le -b^2. \tag{A.14}$$

On the other hand, if for some $t \in (0,1)$, $\|V(\eta(t,u))\| > 1$, $h(\|V(\eta(t,u))\|) = \|V(\eta(t,u))\|^{-1}$ so (A.1)(i) and (A.13) yield

$$\frac{dI(\eta(t,u))}{dt} \le -\frac{1}{4}. \tag{A.15}$$

Consequently for all $t \in (0,1)$, we have

$$\frac{dI(\eta(t,u))}{dt} \le -\min\left(b^2, \frac{1}{4}\right). \tag{A.16}$$

Integrating (A.16) and combining the result with (A.11) gives

$$\min(b^2, \tfrac{1}{4}) \le I(u) - I(\eta(t,u)) \le 2\hat{\varepsilon}$$

which is contrary to (A.6).

The proof of Theorem A.4 is complete.

REMARKS A.17. (i) Note that the full strength of (PS) was not required in the above proof. We only needed (PS) to conclude that K_c was compact and that (A.5) holds for some $b, \hat{\varepsilon} > 0$. But we can also achieve this by merely assuming $(\mathrm{PS})_{\mathrm{loc}}$: there is a $\delta > 0$ such that $|I(u_n) - c| < \delta$ and $I'(u_n) \to 0$ as $n \to \infty$ implies that (u_n) is precompact. Still weaker forms of (PS) have been found (see e.g. [**Ce**, **Ch1**]).

(ii) It is sometimes useful to have a bit more flexibility in the definition of a p.g. vector. If (A.1) is replaced by

$$\text{(A.1}'\text{)}\qquad \begin{array}{ll} \text{(i)} & \|v\| \le \alpha \|I'(u)\|, \\ \text{(ii)} & I'(u)v \ge \beta \|I'(u)\|^2, \end{array}$$

where $0 < \beta < \alpha$, it is easy to check that Lemma A.2 holds with w chosen so that $I'(u)w > 2\beta(\alpha+\beta)^{-1}\|w\|$ and $z = (\alpha+\beta)2^{-1}\|I'(u)w\|$. Moreover the proof of Theorem A.4 also is essentially unchanged aside from replacing (A.6) by

$$\text{(A.6}'\text{)}\qquad 0 < \hat{\varepsilon} < \min\left(\bar{\varepsilon}, \frac{\beta b \delta}{16\alpha}, \frac{b^2}{2}, \frac{1}{4\alpha^2}\right).$$

(iii) There are problems where instead of $\eta(t,u)$ satisfying 5°–7° (as well as the other conclusions of Theorem A.4), one wants a function $\tilde{\eta}(1,u)$ to satisfy $I(\tilde{\eta}(1,u)) \ge I(u)$, and if

$$\tilde{A}_s \equiv \{u \in E \,|\, I(u) \ge s\},$$

then $\tilde{\eta}(1, \tilde{A}_{c-\varepsilon} \setminus \mathcal{O}) \subset \tilde{A}_{c+\varepsilon}$ (with $\mathcal{O} = \varnothing$ if $K_c = \varnothing$). Such an $\tilde{\eta}$ can be obtained by slightly modifying the proof just given, in particular using a positive rather than a negative gradient flow.

(iv) There are versions of Theorem A.4 for a functional I defined on a Banach manifold, $\mathcal{M}$, rather than a Banach space [**Br1**, **P1–2**, **S1–2**]. Using the same sort of ideas as in the proof of Theorem A.4, and in particular constructing a p.g. vector field for $\mathcal{M}$ which is tangential to $\mathcal{M}$, we can get an analogue of Theorem A.4 for such a setting. E.g. in Chapter 7 we consider the case of $\mathcal{M}$ a sphere, say $\partial B_1(0)$, in a Hilbert space. For this special case, a tangential p.g. vector field can be constructed via $V(x) - (V(x) \cdot x)x$, where $V(x)$ is a p.g. vector field for I on E.

The next result concerns the effect on the mapping $\eta(1,u)$ of making stronger assumptions on the form of I. Such information is useful in particular for highly indefinite functionals such as arise in treating Hamiltonian systems as in Chapter 6.

PROPOSITION A.18. *Suppose E is a real Hilbert space and $I \in C^1(E, \mathbf{R})$ with $I(u) = \frac{1}{2}(Lu, u) + \varphi(u)$, L is selfadjoint, and φ' is compact. Then*

$$\eta(t,u) = e^{\theta(t,u)L}u + K(t,u),$$

where $0 \le \theta(t,u) \le 1$ and $K\colon [0,1] \times E \to E$ is compact.

PROOF. By the proof of Theorem A.4, η is determined as the solution of the initial value problem

$$\frac{d\eta}{dt} = -\omega(\eta)V(\eta), \qquad \eta(0,u) = u, \tag{A.19}$$

where $0 \le \omega \le 1$ and V is a p.g. vector field for I' on $\tilde{E}$. Actually since $\omega(\xi) = f(\xi)g(\xi)h(\|V(\xi)\|)$ and $f(\xi)g(\xi) = 0$ if $I(\xi) \notin [c-\hat{\varepsilon}, c+\hat{\varepsilon}]$ or if $u \in N_{\delta/8}$, V need only be a p.g. vector field on $S \equiv \{\xi \in E | I(\xi) \in [c-\hat{\varepsilon}, c+\hat{\varepsilon}]$ and $\xi \notin N_{\delta/8}\}$. We claim such a V can be chosen so that $V(u) = Lu + W(u)$ where W is compact. Assuming this for the moment, (A.19) becomes

$$\frac{d\eta}{dt} + \omega(\eta)L\eta = -\omega(\eta)W(\eta). \tag{A.20}$$

Considering the η in the argument of ω and W as being known, η satisfies an inhomogeneous linear equation and therefore it can be represented as

$$\eta(t,u) = \exp\left(\left(\int_0^t -\omega(\eta(s,u))\,ds\right) L\right) u + K(t,u), \tag{A.21}$$

where

$$K(t,u) = -\int_0^t \left[\exp\left(\int_0^\tau \omega(\eta(s,u))\,ds\right) L\right] \omega(\eta(\tau,u))W(\eta(\tau,u))\,d\tau. \tag{A.22}$$

To see that $K\colon [0,1] \times E \to E$ is compact, suppose $B \subset E$ is bounded. Without loss of generality, $B = B_R$ for some $R > 0$. By 4° of Proposition A.4, $\eta([0,1] \times B_R) \subset B_{R+1}$. Therefore $W(\eta([0,1] \times B_R)) \subset W(B_{R+1}) \subset \overline{W(B_{R+1})}$ which is compact. Let

$$Y \equiv \{e^{-\alpha L}\beta z | \alpha, \beta \in [0,1], z \in \overline{W(B_{R+1})}\}.$$

Since the map

$$(\alpha, \beta, z) \to e^{-\alpha L}\beta z$$

is a continuous function on the compact set $[0,1]^2 \times \overline{W(B_{R+1})}$, its range Y is compact. Therefore the closed convex hull $\hat{Y}$ of Y is also compact. Now recalling that $0 \le \omega(\xi) \le 1$, for each $\tau \in [0,1]$ and $u \in B_R$,

$$Z(\tau) \equiv \exp\left[\left(\int_0^\tau \omega(\eta(s,u))\,ds\right) L\right] \omega(\eta(\tau,u))W(\eta(\tau,u)) \in Y.$$

Hence for $t \in [0,1]$,

$$\int_0^t Z\,d\tau \in \hat{Y}.$$

It follows that K is compact.

To complete the proof of Proposition A.18, we must show it is possible to choose a p.g. vector field V for I' on S such that $V(u) = Lu + W(u)$, where W is compact. As a first step we have:

PROPOSITION A.23. *Let E be a Hilbert space and $T\colon E \to E$ be compact. Then given any $\gamma > 0$, there exists a $\hat{T}\colon E \to E$ such that $\hat{T}$ is compact, locally Lipschitz continuous, and*

$$\|T(u) - \hat{T}(u)\| \leq \gamma \tag{A.24}$$

for all $u \in E$.

Assuming Proposition A.23 for the moment, let $\gamma = b/2$, where b was defined in (A.5), and let W be the corresponding mapping given by Proposition A.23 with $T(u) = \varphi'(u)$. We claim $V(u) \equiv Lu + W(u)$ is a p.g. vector field on S. It is certainly locally Lipschitz continuous. We will verify (A.1′) for V with $\alpha = 2$, $\beta = \frac{1}{2}$, and $u \in S$. By Proposition A.23, (A.5), and our choice of γ,

$$\begin{aligned}\|V(u)\| &= \|Lu + W(u)\| \leq \|Lu + \varphi'(u)\| + \|\varphi'(u) - W(u)\| \\ &\leq \|I'(u)\| + \gamma \leq \|I'(u)\| + b \leq 2\|I'(u)\|.\end{aligned}$$

Therefore (A.1′)(i) holds. Similarly,

$$\begin{aligned}I'(u)V(u) &= I'(u)(Lu + \varphi'(u) + W(u) - \varphi'(u)) \\ &\geq \|I'(u)\|^2 - \|I'(u)\|\gamma \geq \|I'(u)\|^2 - \tfrac{1}{2}\|I'(u)\|^2 = \tfrac{1}{2}\|I'(u)\|^2.\end{aligned}$$

Thus we have (A.1′)(ii). Finally we can give the

PROOF OF PROPOSITION A.23. (This result is essentially due to Benci [**Be2**].) First we construct a special partition of unity for E and then use it to construct $\hat{T}$. For each $u \in E$, set $S_u \equiv B_1(u) \cap \{v \in E \mid \|T(u) - T(v)\| < \gamma\}$. Then $\{S_u \mid u \in E\}$ is an open covering of E and therefore it possesses a locally finite refinement $\{Y_i\}$. Let $\rho_i(u)$ denote the distance from u to the complement of Y_i and

$$\beta_i(u) \equiv \rho_i(u) \Big/ \sum_j \rho_j(u).$$

Then $\beta_i(u)$ is a (locally Lipschitz continuous) partition of unity as in the proof of Lemma A.2. By construction for each Y_i, there is a $w_i \in E$ such that $Y_i \subset S_{w_i}$. Therefore

$$(T(u) - T(w_i), v) < \gamma\|v\|$$

for all $u \in Y_i$ and $v \in E$. Since $\beta_i(u) \geq 0$ and equals 0 if $u \notin Y_i$,

$$\beta_i(u)(T(u) - T(w_i), u) \leq \gamma\beta_i(u)\|v\|$$

for all $u, v \in E$. Summing over i yields

$$\left(T(u) - \sum_i \beta_i(u)T(w_i), v\right) \leq \gamma\|v\|$$

for all $u, v \in E$. Setting $\hat{T}(u) \equiv \sum_i \beta_i(u)T(w_i)$, it is clear that $\hat{T}$ is locally Lipschitz continuous and satisfies (A.24). Moreover $\hat{T}$ is compact. Indeed let $B \subset E$ be bounded. Without loss of generality, $B = B_R(0)$. Let $u \in B_R(0)$. Then $\hat{T}(u) = \sum_i \beta_i(u)T(w_i)$. If $u \notin Y_i$, $\beta_i(u) = 0$ while if $u \in Y_i$, $u \in S_{w_i}$ and therefore $\|u - w_i\| < 1$. Thus the only nonzero contribution to $\hat{T}(u)$ comes from those terms in the sum where $w_i \in B_{R+1}$. Consequently $\hat{T}(u)$ is a convex combination of terms in $T(B_{R+1})$. Since the convex hull of a compact set is compact, $\hat{T}$ is a compact mapping.

Appendix B

This final appendix treats the question of verifying in applications some of the hypotheses that are required in the abstract theorems presented earlier. In particular sufficient conditions will be given which insure that certain classes of functionals belong to $C^1(E, \mathbf{R})$. Furthermore the verification of the Palais-Smale condition will be simplified for these classes.

We begin with a useful technical result.

PROPOSITION B.1. *Let $\Omega \subset \mathbf{R}^n$ be a bounded domain and let g satisfy*
(g_1) $g \in C(\overline{\Omega} \times \mathbf{R}, \mathbf{R})$, and
(g_2) there are constants $r, s \geq 1$ and $a_1, a_2 \geq 0$ such that

$$|g(x, \xi)| \leq a_1 + a_2 |\xi|^{r/s}$$

for all $x \in \overline{\Omega}$, $\xi \in \mathbf{R}$.

Then the map $\varphi(x) \to g(x, \varphi(x))$ belongs to $C(L^r(\Omega), L^s(\Omega))$.

PROOF. If $u \in L^r(\Omega)$,

$$\begin{aligned}\int_\Omega |g(x, u(x))|^s \, dx &\leq \int_\Omega (a_1 + a_2 |u|^{r/s})^s \, dx \\ &\leq a_3 \int_\Omega (1 + |u|^r) \, dx\end{aligned} \tag{B.2}$$

which shows that $g \colon L^r(\Omega) \to L^s(\Omega)$. To prove the continuity of this map, observe that it is continuous at φ if and only if $f(x, z(x)) = g(x, z(x) + \varphi(x)) - g(x, \varphi(x))$ is continuous at $z = 0$. Therefore we can assume $\varphi = 0$ and $g(x, 0) = 0$. Let $\varepsilon > 0$. We claim there is a $\delta > 0$ such that $\|u\|_{L^r(\Omega)} \leq \delta$ implies $\|g(\cdot, u)\|_{L^s(\Omega)} \leq \varepsilon$. By (g_1) and $g(x, 0) = 0$, given any $\hat{\varepsilon} > 0$, there is a $\hat{\delta} > 0$ such that $|g(x, \xi)| \leq \hat{\varepsilon}$ if $x \subset \overline{\Omega}$ and $|\xi| \leq \hat{\delta}$. Let $u \in L^r(\Omega)$ with $\|u\|_{L^r(\Omega)} \leq \delta$, δ being free for now, and set

$$\Omega_1 \equiv \{x \in \overline{\Omega} \mid |u(x)| \leq \beta\} \quad (= \Omega_1(u)).$$

Therefore

$$\int_{\Omega_1} |g(x, u(x))|^s \, dx \leq \hat{\varepsilon}^s |\Omega_1| \leq \hat{\varepsilon}^s |\Omega|, \tag{B.3}$$

where $|\Omega_1|$ denotes the measure of Ω_1, etc. Choose $\hat{\varepsilon}$ so that $(\hat{\varepsilon})^s|\Omega| \leq (\varepsilon/2)^s$. This determines $\hat{\varepsilon}$. Let $\Omega_2 = \overline{\Omega} \setminus \Omega_1$. Then as in (B.2),

$$\int_{\Omega_2} |g(x, u(x))|^s \, dx \leq a_3(|\Omega_2| + \delta^r). \tag{B.4}$$

Moreover

$$\delta^r \geq \int_{\Omega_2} |u|^r \, dx \geq \beta^r |\Omega_2| \tag{B.5}$$

or $|\Omega_2| \leq (\delta\beta^{-1})^r$. Combining (B.4)–(B.5) gives

$$\int_{\Omega_2} |g(x, u(x))|^s \, ds \leq a_3(1 + \beta^{-r})\delta^r. \tag{B.6}$$

Choose δ so that $a_3(1 + \beta^{-r})\delta^r \leq (\varepsilon/2)^s$. Thus (B.3) and (B.6) imply

$$\|g(\cdot, u)\|_{L^s(\Omega)} \leq \varepsilon \quad \text{if } \|u\|_{L^r(\Omega)} \leq \delta$$

and the proof is complete.

The next result is a standard version of the Sobolev Embedding Theorem. The space $W_0^{1,2}(\Omega)$ was defined in Chapter 1 and its norm will be denoted by $\|\cdot\|$.

PROPOSITION B.7. *Let Ω be a bounded domain in $\mathbf{R}^n$ whose boundary is a smooth manifold. If $u \in W_0^{1,2}(\Omega)$, then $u \in L^{2n/n-2}(\Omega)$ (where $n \geq 3$) and there is a constant $c > 0$ such that*

$$\|u\|_{L^t(\Omega)} \leq c\|u\| \tag{B.8}$$

for all $t \in [1, 2n(n-2)^{-1}]$ and for all $u \in W_0^{1,2}(\Omega)$. Moreover the embedding map $W_0^{1,2}(\Omega) \to L^t(\Omega)$, $u \to u$ is compact for $t \in [1, 2n(n-2)^{-1})$.

PROOF. See e.g. [**N1** or **F**].

REMARK B.9. If $n = 1$ or 2, stronger statements can be made. In particular (B.8) holds for all $t \in [1, \infty]$ for $n = 1$ while for $n = 2$ it is valid for all $t \in [1, \infty)$ with c depending on t.

Now a criterion can be given showing that an important class of functionals which arise in studying second order semilinear elliptic boundary value problems belong to $C^1(W_0^{1,2}(\Omega), \mathbf{R})$. (A related result is given in [**BR**].)

PROPOSITION B.10. *Let Ω be a bounded domain in $\mathbf{R}^n$ whose boundary is a smooth manifold. Let p satisfy*

(p_1) $p(x, \xi) \in C(\overline{\Omega} \times \mathbf{R}, \mathbf{R})$, and

(p_2) there are constants $a_1, a_2 > 0$ such that

$$|p(x, \xi)| \leq a_1 + a_2|\xi|^s,$$

where $0 \leq s < (n+2)(n-2)^{-1}$ and $n \geq 3$. If

$$P(x, \xi) \equiv \int_0^\xi p(x, t) \, dt$$

and

$$I(u) \equiv \int_\Omega (\tfrac{1}{2}|\nabla u|^2 - P(x,u))\,dx, \tag{B.11}$$

then $I \in C^1(W_0^{1,2}(\Omega), \mathbf{R})$ *and*

$$I'(u)\varphi = \int_\Omega (\nabla u \cdot \nabla \varphi - p(x,u)\varphi)\,dx \tag{B.12}$$

for all $\varphi \in E \equiv W_0^{1,2}(\Omega)$. *Moreover*

$$J(u) \equiv \int_\Omega P(x,u(x))\,dx \tag{B.13}$$

is weakly continuous and $J'(u)$ *is compact.*

PROOF. By Proposition B.7, (p_1) and (p_2), I is defined on E and the same is true for $I'(u)$ with the aid of the Hölder inequality. It is clear that the first term in I is C^1 (even C^∞) and its Fréchet derivative is the first term in I'. Hence we must show

$$J(u) \equiv \int_\Omega P(x,u(x))\,dx$$

belongs to $C^1(E, \mathbf{R})$. This will be accomplished in two steps: First showing that J is Fréchet differentiable on E (and therefore is Lipschitz continuous) and then proving that $J'(u)$ is continuous.

To begin, let $u, \varphi \in E$. We claim: given any $\varepsilon > 0$, there exists a $\delta = \delta(\varepsilon, u)$ such that

$$\left| J(u+\varphi) - J(u) - \int_\Omega p(x,u)\varphi\,dx \right| \le \varepsilon \|\varphi\| \tag{B.14}$$

provided that $\|\varphi\| \le \delta$. Therefore J is Fréchet differentiable at u and J' is given by the appropriate term in (B.12). In fact the argument given below shows more: $\delta = \delta(\varepsilon, \|u\|)$ and hence J is uniformly differentiable on bounded sets in the sense of Krasnoselski [**K**].

Setting

$$\Psi \equiv |P(x,u(x)+\varphi(x)) - P(x,u(x)) - p(x,u(x))\varphi(x)|,$$

we have

$$\left| J(u+\varphi) - J(u) - \int_\Omega p(x,u)\varphi\,dx \right| \le \int_\Omega \Psi\,dx. \tag{B.15}$$

Define

$$\Omega_1 \equiv \{x \in \overline{\Omega} \mid |u(x)| \ge \beta\},$$
$$\Omega_2 \equiv \{x \in \overline{\Omega} \mid |\varphi(x)| \ge \gamma\},$$
$$\Omega_3 \equiv \{x \in \overline{\Omega} \mid |u(x)| \le \beta \text{ and } |\varphi(x)| \le \gamma\}$$

with β and γ free for the moment. Therefore

$$\int_\Omega \Psi\,dx \le \sum_{i=1}^{3} \int_{\Omega_i} \Psi\,dx. \tag{B.16}$$

By the Mean Value Theorem,

$$P(x,\xi+\eta)-P(x,\xi)=p(x,\xi+\theta\eta)\eta, \tag{B.17}$$

where $\theta\in(0,1)$. Therefore by (B.17), (p_2), and the Hölder inquality,

$$\begin{aligned}
&\int_{\Omega_1}|P(x,u(x)+\varphi(x))-P(x,u(x))|\,dx\\
&\le\int_{\Omega_1}[a_1+a_2(|u(x)|+|\varphi(x)|)^s|\varphi(x)|]\,dx\\
&\le a_1|\Omega_1|^{(n+2)/2n}\|\varphi\|_{L^{2n/n-2}(\Omega)}\\
&\quad+a_3|\Omega_1|^{1/\sigma}[\|u\|^s_{L^{s+1}(\Omega)}+\|\varphi\|^s_{L^{s+1}(\Omega)}]\|\varphi\|_{L^{2n/n-2}(\Omega)},
\end{aligned} \tag{B.18}$$

where

$$\frac{1}{\sigma}+\frac{s}{s+1}+\frac{n-2}{2n}=1. \tag{B.19}$$

Observe that $s<(n+2)(n-2)^{-1}$ implies that $s(s+1)^{-1}+(n-2)(2n)^{-1}<1$ so there exists a $\sigma>1$ satisfying (B.19) and justifying (B.18). Combining (B.8) and (B.18) shows

$$\begin{aligned}
&\int_{\Omega_1}|P(x,u(x)+\varphi(x))-P(x,u(x))|\,dx\\
&\le a_4\|\varphi\|[|\Omega_1|^{(n+2)/2n}+|\Omega_1|^{1/\sigma}(\|u\|^s+\|\varphi\|^s)].
\end{aligned} \tag{B.20}$$

Similarly

$$\int_{\Omega_1}|p(x,u(x))\varphi(x)|\,dx\le a_5\|\varphi\|[|\Omega_1|^{(n+2)/2n}+|\Omega_1|^{1/\sigma}\|u\|^s]. \tag{B.21}$$

By (B.8) and the Hölder inequality,

$$\|u\|\ge a_6\|u\|_{L^2(\Omega)}\ge a_6\|u\|_{L^2(\Omega_1)}\ge a_6\beta|\Omega_1|^{1/2}. \tag{B.22}$$

Therefore

$$|\Omega_1|^{1/\sigma}\le\left(\frac{\|u\|}{a_6\beta}\right)^{2/\sigma}\equiv M_1,\qquad |\Omega_1|^{(n+2)/2n}\le\left(\frac{\|u\|}{a_6\beta}\right)^{(n+2)/n}\equiv M_2, \tag{B.23}$$

where $M_1,M_2\to 0$ as $\beta\to\infty$. Combining (B.18)–(B.23) yields

$$\int_{\Omega_1}\Psi\,dx\le a_7[M_2+M_1(\|u\|^s+\|\varphi\|^s)]\|\varphi\|. \tag{B.24}$$

We can assume $\delta\le 1$. Further choose β so large that $a_7[M_2+M_1(\|u\|^s+1)]\le\varepsilon/3$. Hence

$$\int_{\Omega_1}\Psi\,dx\le\frac{\varepsilon}{3}\|\varphi\|. \tag{B.25}$$

Similar estimates to those above show

(B.26)

$$\begin{aligned}\int_{\Omega_2} \Psi\, dx &\le a_3 \int_{\Omega_2} [1 + (|u(x)| + |\varphi(x)|)^s |\varphi(x)|]\, dx \\ &\le a_4 \left(\int_{\Omega_2} [1 + (|u(x)| + |\varphi(x)|)^s]^{(s+1)/s}\, dx \right)^{s/(s+1)} \|\varphi\|_{L^{s+1}(\Omega_2)} \\ &\le a_5 (1 + \|u\|^s + \|\varphi\|^s) \left(\int_{\Omega_2} |\varphi(x)|^{s+1} \left(\frac{|\varphi(x)|}{\gamma} \right)^{m-(s+1)} dx \right)^{1/s+1},\end{aligned}$$

where $m = 2n(n-2)^{-1} > s+1$. Therefore

$$\int_{\Omega_2} \Psi\, dx \le a_6 \gamma^{(s+1-m)/(s+1)} (1 + \|u\|^s + \|\varphi\|^s) \|\varphi\|^{m/(s+1)}. \tag{B.27}$$

Next since $P \in C^1(\overline{\Omega} \times \mathbf{R}, \mathbf{R})$, given any $\hat{\varepsilon}, \hat{\beta} > 0$, there exists a $\hat{\gamma} = \hat{\gamma}(\hat{\varepsilon}, \hat{\beta})$ such that

$$|P(x, \xi + h) - P(x, \xi) - p(x, \xi) h| \le \hat{\varepsilon} |h| \tag{B.28}$$

whenever $x \in \overline{\Omega}$, $|\xi| \le \hat{\beta}$, and $|h| \le \hat{\gamma}$. In particular if $\hat{\beta} \equiv \beta$ and $\gamma \le \hat{\gamma}$, (B.8) and (B.28) imply:

$$\int_{\Omega_3} \Psi\, dx \le \hat{\varepsilon} \int_{\Omega_3} |\varphi(x)|\, dx \le a_7 \hat{\varepsilon} \|\varphi\|. \tag{B.29}$$

Choose $\hat{\varepsilon}$ so that $3a_7 \hat{\varepsilon} \le \varepsilon$. This determines $\hat{\gamma}$. Choose $\gamma = \hat{\gamma}$. Combining (B.16), (B.25), (B.27), and (B.29) yields

$$\int_{\Omega} \Psi\, dx \le \frac{2\varepsilon}{3} \|\varphi\| + a_6 \gamma^{(s+1-m)/(s+1)} (1 + \|u\|^s + \|\varphi\|^s) \|\varphi\|^{m/(s+1)}. \tag{B.30}$$

Finally choose δ so small that

$$a_6 \gamma^{1-m/(s+1)} (2 + \|u\|^s) \delta^{(m/(s+1))-1} \le \frac{\varepsilon}{3} \tag{B.31}$$

thereby obtaining (B.14).

To prove that $J'(u)$ is continuous, let $u_m \to u$ in E. Then $u_m \to u$ in $L^{s+1}(\Omega)$ via (B.8). By the Hölder inequality and (B.8) again,

$$\begin{aligned}\|J'(u_m) - J'(u)\| &= \sup_{\|\varphi\| \le 1} \left| \int_{\Omega} (p(x, u_m(x)) - p(x, \varphi(x))) \varphi(x)\, dx \right| \\ &\le a_7 \|p(\cdot, u_m) - p(\cdot, u)\|_{L^{s+1/s}(\Omega)}.\end{aligned} \tag{B.32}$$

By (p_2),

$$|p(x, \xi)| \le a_1 + a_2 |\xi|^{\alpha s/\alpha}$$

for any $\alpha \ge 1$ and all $x \in \overline{\Omega}$, $\xi \in \mathbf{R}$. Hence Proposition B.1 implies $p \in C(L^{\alpha s}(\Omega), L^{\alpha}(\Omega))$. Choosing $\alpha = (s+1)s^{-1}$, we see the right-hand side of (B.32) tends to 0 as $m \to \infty$ and J' is continuous.

Finally to prove that J is weakly continuous, let u_m converge weakly to u in E. Then by Proposition B.7, u_m converges to u in $L^{s+1}(\Omega)$ since $s+1 < 2n(n-2)^{-1}$

via (p_2). Consequently Proposition B.1 implies $J(u_m) \to J(u)$. Since J is weakly continuous and J' is uniformly differentiable on bounded subsets of E, an abstract theorem [**K**] implies J' is compact. (Alternatively, let (u_m) be bounded in E. Then along a subsequence, u_m converges weakly to some $u \in E$ and $u_m \to u$ in $L^{s+1}(\Omega)$ via Proposition B.7. The proof then concludes via (B.32) and the sentences which follow it.)

REMARK B.33. The ideas that were used in the proof of Proposition B.10 can be employed to prove related regularity results. E.g.:

PROPOSITION B.34. *Let Ω be a bounded domain in $\mathbf{R}^n$ whose boundary is a smooth manifold. Let p satisfy*

$(\hat{p}_1)$ $p \in C^1(\overline{\Omega} \times \mathbf{R}, \mathbf{R})$, *and*

$(\hat{p}_2)$ *there are constants $a_1, a_2 > 0$ such that*

$$|p_\xi(x,\xi)| \le a_1 + a_2|\xi|^{s-1}$$

where $0 \le s < (n+2)(n-2)^{-1}$ and $n \ge 3$. If

$$P(x,\xi) \equiv \int_0^\xi p(x,t)\,dt$$

and

$$I(u) \equiv \int_\Omega \left(\tfrac{1}{2}|\nabla u|^2 - P(x,u(x))\right) dx,$$

then $I \in C^2(W_0^{1,2}(\Omega), \mathbf{R})$, I' is given by (B.12), *and*

$$I''(u)(\varphi,\psi) = \int_\Omega (\nabla\varphi \cdot \nabla\psi - p_\xi(x,u)\varphi\psi)\,dx$$

for all $\varphi, \psi \in W_0^{1,2}(\Omega)$.

The next result concerns the verification of (PS). Recall that (PS) requires any sequence (u_m) such that (i) $I(u_m)$ is bounded and (ii) $I'(u_m) \to 0$ as $m \to \infty$ to be precompact. According to the following result in the setting of functionals like (B.11), to get (PS), it suffices to show that (i) and (ii) imply (u_m) is a bounded sequence.

PROPOSITION B.35. *Let p satisfy (p_1)–(p_2) and let I be defined by* (B.11). *If (u_m) is a bounded sequence in $E \equiv W_0^{1,2}(\Omega)$ such that $I'(u_m) \to 0$ as $m \to \infty$, then (u_m) has a convergent subsequence.*

PROOF. Let $D\colon E \to E^*$ denote the duality map between E and its dual. Then for $u, \varphi \in E$,

$$(Du)\varphi = \int_\Omega \nabla u \cdot \nabla\varphi\,dx.$$

Thus

$$D^{-1}I'(u) = u - D^{-1}J'(u). \tag{B.36}$$

Due to the form of this map, the conclusion of the proposition follows if we can show $J'(u_m)$ has a convergent subsequence. Indeed the continuity of D^{-1} and (B.36) then imply

$$u_m = D^{-1}I'(u_m) + D^{-1}J'(u_m) \to \lim D^{-1}J'(u_m),$$

the limit being taken along the convergent subsequence of $J'(u_m)$. But since (u_m) is bounded in E and by Proposition B.10, J' is compact, $J'(u_m)$ has a convergent subsequence and the proof is complete.

In Chapter 6 which studies the existence of periodic solutions of Hamiltonian systems, an analogue of Proposition B.10 is needed. The space $E \equiv W^{1/2,2}(S^1, \mathbf{R}^{2n})$ is defined in Chapter 6. For this space we have

PROPOSITION B.37. *Let $H \in C^1(\mathbf{R}^{2n}, \mathbf{R})$ and satisfy*

$$|H(\varsigma)| \leq a_1 + a_2|\varsigma|^s \tag{B.38}$$

for some $s \in [1, \infty)$ and for all $\varsigma \in \mathbf{R}^{2n}$. Then

$$J(z) \equiv \int_0^{2\pi} H(z(t))\, dt \in C^1(E, \mathbf{R}) \tag{B.39}$$

with

$$J'(z)w = \int_0^{2\pi} H_z(z(t))w(t)\, dt$$

for $w \in E$. Moreover $J'(z)$ is compact.

PROOF. Given Proposition 6.6 and (B.38) the proof is almost identical to that of Proposition B.10. We therefore omit the details (see also [**BR**]).

References

[**Ag**] S. Agmon, *The L^p approach to the Dirichlet problem*, Ann. Scuola Norm. Sup. Pisa **13** (1959), 405–448.

[**ALP**] S. Ahmad, A. C. Lazer and J. L. Paul, *Elementary critical point theory and perturbations of elliptic boundary value problems at resonance*, Indiana Univ. Math. J. **25** (1976), 933–944.

[**Am**] H. Amann, *Saddle points and multiple solutions of differential equations*, Math. Z. **196** (1979), 127–166.

[**AZ**] H. Amann and E. Zehnder, *Nontrivial solutions for a class of nonresonance problems and applications to nonlinear differential equations*, Ann. Scuola Norm. Sup. Pisa Cl. Sci. (4) **7** (1980), 539–603.

[**A**] A. Ambrosetti, *On the existence of multiple solutions for a class of nonlinear boundary value problems*, Rend. Sem. Mat. Univ. Padova **49** (1973), 195–204.

[**AM1**] A. Ambrosetti and G. Mancini, *On a theorem by Ekeland and Lasry concerning the number of periodic Hamiltonian trajectories*, J. Differential Equations **43** (1981), 1–6.

[**AM2**] ——, *Solutions of minimal period for a class of convex Hamiltonian systems*, Math. Ann. **255** (1981), 405–421.

[**AR**] A. Ambrosetti and P. H. Rabinowitz, *Dual variational methods in critical point theory and applications*, J. Funct. Anal. **14** (1973), 349–381.

[**Ba**] A. Bahri, *Topological results on a certain class of functionals and applications*, J. Funct. Anal. **41** (1981), 397–427.

[**BB**] A. Bahri and H. Berestycki, *A perturbation method in critical point theory and applications*, Trans. Amer. Math. Soc. **267** (1981), 1–32.

[**BL**] A. Bahri and P. L. Lions, *Remarks on the variational theory of critical points and applications*, C. R. Acad. Sci. Paris Sér. I Math. **301** (1985), 145–148.

[**Be1**] V. Benci, *Some critical point theorems and applications*, Comm. Pure Appl. Math. **33** (1980), 147–172.

[**Be2**] ——, *On critical point theory for indefinite functionals in the presence of symmetries*, Trans. Amer. Math. Soc. **274** (1982), 533–572.

[**Be3**] ——, *A geometrical index for the group* S^1 *and some applications to the research of periodic solutions of O.D.E.'s*, Comm. Pure Appl. Math. **34** (1981), 393–432.

[**BF**] V. Benci and D. Fortunato, *The dual method in critical point theory: Multiplicity results for indefinite functionals*, Ann. Mat. Pura Appl. (4) **32** (1982), 215–242.

[**BR**] V. Benci and P. H. Rabinowitz, *Critical point theorems for indefinite functionals*, Invent. Math. **52** (1979), 241–273.

[**BLMR**] H. Berestycki, J. M. Lasry, G. Mancini and B. Ruf, *Existence of multiple periodic orbits on star-shaped Hamiltonian surfaces*, Comm. Pure Appl. Math. **38** (1985), 253–290.

[**Bg**] M. S. Berger, *Nonlinearity and functional analysis*, Academic Press, New York, 1978.

[**BW**] M. S. Berger and M. S. Berger, *Perspectives in nonlinearity*, Benjamin, New York, 1968.

[**Bi**] G. D. Birkhoff, *Dynamical systems with two degrees of freedom*, Trans. Amer. Math. Soc. **18** (1917), 199–300.

[**Bö**] R. Böhme, *Die Lösung der Verzwergungsgleichungen für nichtlineare Eigenwertprobleme*, Math. Z. **127** (1972), 105–126.

[**BN**] H. Brezis and L. Nirenberg, *Positive solutions of nonlinear elliptic equations involving critical Sobolev exponents*, Comm. Pure Appl. Math. **36** (1983), 437–477.

[**Br1**] F. E. Browder, *Infinite dimensional manifolds and nonlinear eigenvalue problems*, Ann. of Math. (2) **82** (1965), 459–477.

[**Br2**] ——, *Nonlinear eigenvalues and group invariance*, Functional Analysis and Related Fields (F. E. Browder, ed.), Springer-Verlag, Berlin and New York, 1970, pp. 1–58.

[**CL**] A. Castro and A. C. Lazer, *Applications of a maximin principle*, Rev. Colombiana Mat. **10** (1976), 141–149.

[**Ce**] G. Cerami, *Un criterio di esistenza per i punti critici su varieta illimitate*, Rend. Acad. Sci. Let. Ist. Lombardo **112** (1978), 332–336.

[**Ch1**] K. C. Chang, *Variational methods for nondifferentiable functionals and their applications to partial differential equations*, J. Math. Anal. Appl. **80** (1981), 102–129.

[**Ch2**] ——, *Morse theory on Banach space and its applications to partial differential equations*, preprint.

[**C**] D. C. Clark, *A variant of the Ljusternik-Schnirelmann theory*, Indiana Univ. Math. J. **22** (1972), 65–74.

[**Co1**] C. V. Coffman, *A minimum-maximum principle for a class of nonlinear integral equations*, J. Analyse Math. **22** (1969), 391–419.

[**Co2**] ——, *On a class of nonlinear elliptic boundary value problems*, J. Math. Mech. **19** (1970), 351–356.

[CC] C. C. Conley, *Isolated invariant sets and the Morse index*, CBMS Regional Conf. Ser. in Math., no. 38, Amer. Math. Soc., Providence, R. I., 1978.

[CF] P. E. Conner and E. E. Floyd, *Fixed point free involutions and equivariant maps*, Bull. Amer. Math. Soc. **66** (1966), 416–441.

[CH] R. Courant and D. Hilbert, *Methods of mathematical physics*, Vols. I and II, Interscience, New York, 1953 and 1962.

[CR] M. G. Crandall and P. H. Rabinowitz, *Continuation and variational methods for the existence of positive solutions of nonlinear elliptic eigenvalue problems*, Arch. Rat. Mech. Anal. **58** (1975), 201–218.

[De] S. Deng, *Minimal periodic solutions for a class of Hamiltonian equations*, China University of Science and Technology, preprint.

[D1] J. Dieudonné, *Foundations of modern analysis*, Academic Press, New York, 1960.

[DL] G. C. Dong and S. Li, *On the existence of infinitely many solutions of the Dirichlet problem for some nonlinear elliptic equations*, Sci. Sinica Ser. A **25** (1982), 468–475.

[EH] I. Ekeland and H. Hofer, *Periodic solutions with prescribed minimal period for convex autonomous Hamiltonian systems*, Invent. Math. **81** (1985), 155–188.

[EL] I. Ekeland and J.-M. Lasry, *On the number of periodic trajectories for a Hamiltonian flow on a convex energy surface*, Ann. of Math. (2) **112** (1980), 283–319.

[FH] E. R. Fadell and S. Husseini, *Relative cohomological index theories*, Advances in Math. (to appear).

[FHR] E. R. Fadell, S. Husseini and P. H. Rabinowitz, *Borsuk-Ulam theorems for arbitrary S^1 actions and applications*, Trans. Amer. Math. Soc. **274** (1982), 345–360.

[FR1] E. R. Fadell and P. H. Rabinowitz, *Bifurcation for odd potential operators and an alternative topological index*, J. Funct. Anal. **26** (1977), 48–67.

[FR2] ——, *Generalized cohomological index theories for Lie group actions with applications to bifurcation questions for Hamiltonian systems*, Invent. Math. **45** (1978), 139–174.

[Fr] A. Friedman, *Partial differential equations*, Holt, Rinehart, and Winston, Inc., New York, 1969.

[G] J. V. A. Goncalves, *A multiplicity result for a semilinear Dirichlet problem*, Houston J. Math. (to appear).

[He1] J. A. Hempel, *Superlinear variational boundary value problems and nonuniqueness*, thesis, University of New England, Australia, 1970.

[He2] ——, *Multiple solutions for a class of nonlinear boundary value problems*, Indiana Univ. Math. J. **20** (1971), 983–996.

[Ho1] H. Hofer, *On strongly indefinite functionals with applications*, Trans. Amer. Math. Soc. **275** (1983), 185–214.

[**Ho2**] ——, *A geometric description of the neighborhood of a critical point given by the Mountain Pass Theorem*, J. London Math. Soc. (2) **31** (1985), 566–570.

[**K**] M. A. Krasnoselski, *Topological methods in the theory of nonlinear integral equations*, Macmillan, New York, 1964.

[**LJS**] J. Leray and J. Schauder, *Topologie et equations fonctionelles*, Ann. Sci. Ecole Norm. Sup. (3) **51** (1934), 45–78.

[**LLS**] L. Ljusternik and L. Schnirelmann, *Methodes topologique dans les problémes variationnels*, Hermann and Cie, Paris, 1934.

[**Ma**] A. Marino, *La biforcazione nel caso variazionale*, Confer. Sem. Mat. Univ. Bari **132** (1977).

[**Mi**] J. Milnor, *Morse theory*, Princeton Univ. Press, Princeton, N. J., 1963.

[**Ni**] W. M. Ni, *Some minimax principles and their applications in nonlinear elliptic equations*, J. Analyse Math. **37** (1980), 248–275.

[**N1**] L. Nirenberg, *On elliptic partial differential equations*, Ann. Scuola Norm. Sup. Pisa (3) **13** (1959), 1–48.

[**N2**] ——, *Variational and topological methods in nonlinear problems*, Bull. Amer. Math. Soc. (N.S.) **4** (1981), 267–302.

[**P1**] R. S. Palais, *Lusternik-Schnirelmann theory on Banach manifolds*, Topology **5** (1966), 115–132.

[**P2**] ——, *Critical point theory and the minimax principle*, Proc. Sympos. Pure Math., vol 15, Amer. Math. Soc., Providence, R. I., 1970, pp. 185–212.

[**Po**] S. I. Pohozaev, *Eigenfunctions of the equation* $\Delta u + \lambda f(u) = 0$, Soviet Math. **5** (1965), 1408–1411.

[**PS**] P. Pucci and J. Serrin, *Extensions of the mountain pass theorem*, Univ. of Minnesota Math. Rep., 83-150 (to appear).

[**R1**] P. H. Rabinowitz, *A note on nonlinear eigenvalue problems for a class of differential equations*, J. Differential Equations **9** (1971), 536–548.

[**R2**] ——, *Variational methods for nonlinear eigenvalue problems*, Eigenvalues of Nonlinear Problems (G. Prodi, ed.), C.I.M.E., Edizioni Cremonese, Roma, 1975, pp. 141–195.

[**R3**] ——, *A bifurcation theorem for potential operators*, J. Funct. Anal. **25** (1977), 412–424.

[**R4**] ——, *Some minimax theorems and applications to nonlinear partial differential equations*, Nonlinear Analysis: A collection of papers in honor of Erich Röthe, Academic Press, New York, 1978, pp. 161–177.

[**R5**] ——, *Some critical point theorems and applications to semilinear elliptic partial differential equations*, Ann. Scuola Norm. Sup. Pisa Cl. Sci. (4) **5** (1978), 215–223.

[**R6**] ——, *Periodic solutions of Hamiltonian systems*, Comm. Pure Appl. Math. **31** (1978), 157–184.

[**R7**] ____, *A variational method for finding periodic solutions of differential equations*, Nonlinear Evolution Equations (M. G. Crandall, ed.), Academic Press, New York, 1978, pp. 225–251.

[**R8**] ____, *Multiple critical points of perturbed symmetric functionals*, Trans. Amer. Math. Soc. **272** (1982), 753–770.

[**R9**] ____, *Periodic solutions of large norm of Hamiltonian systems*, J. Differential Equations **50** (1983), 33–48.

[**S1**] J. T. Schwartz, *Generalizing the Lusternik-Schnirelmann theory of critical points*, Comm. Pure Appl. Math. **17** (1964), 307–315.

[**S2**] ____, *Nonlinear functional analysis*, Gordon & Breach, New York, 1969.

[**Sm**] J. Smoller, *Shock waves and reaction-diffusion equations*, Springer-Verlag, New York, 1982.

[**St1**] M. Struwe, *Infinitely many critical points for functionals which are not even and applications to superlinear boundary value problems*, Manuscripta Math. **32** (1980), 335–364.

[**St2**] ____, *A note on a result of Ambrosetti and Mancini*, Ann. Mat. Pura Appl. **131** (1982), 107–115.

[**Va**] M. M. Vainberg, *Variational methods for the study of nonlinear operators*, Holden-Day, San Francisco, 1964.

[**VG**] E. W. C. van Groesen, *Existence of multiple normal mode trajectories of even classical Hamiltonian systems*, J. Differential Equations **57** (1985), 70–89.

[**W**] A. Weinstein, *Periodic orbits for convex Hamiltonian systems*, Ann. of Math. (2) **108** (1978), 507–518.

[**Wh**] G. T. Whyburn, *Topological analysis*, Princeton Math. Ser., No. 23, Princeton Univ. Press, Princeton, N. J., 1958.

[**Y**] C. T. Yang, *On the theorems of Borsuk-Ulam, Kakutani-Yamabe-Yujobô, and Dysin.* I and II, Ann. of Math. (2) **60** (1954), 262–282 and **62** (1955), 271–180.

BCDEFGHIJ-898